Homework Helpers
Science

Ages 9–10
Key Stage 2/Year 5

Andy Bailey, Jane Harris & Michael Wilkinson

We're the Homework Helpers!

We've thought up lots of fun activities for you!

So grab your pens and pencils...

...and let's get started!

Longman

An imprint of **Pearson Education**

Harlow, England · London · New York · Reading, Massachusetts · San Francisco
Toronto · Don Mills, Ontario · Sydney · Tokyo · Singapore · Hong Kong · Seoul
Taipei · Cape Town · Madrid · Mexico City · Amsterdam · Munich · Paris · Milan

Series editors:
Stuart Wall & Geoff Black
With thanks to Jane Webster for additional material

These people helped us write the book!

A complete range of **Homework Helpers** is available.

		ENGLISH	MATHS	SCIENCE
Key Stage 1	Ages 5–6 Year 1	✓	✓	Science is not included in the National Tests at Key Stage 1
Key Stage 1	Ages 6–7 Year 2	✓	✓	
Key Stage 2	Ages 7–8 Year 3	✓	✓	✓
Key Stage 2	Ages 8–9 Year 4	✓	✓	✓
Key Stage 2	Ages 9–10 Year 5	✓	✓	✓
Key Stage 2	Ages 10–11 Year 6	✓	✓	✓

This tells you about all our other books.

Which ones have you got?

Pearson Education Limited
Edinburgh Gate, Harlow
Essex CM20 2JE, England
and Associated Companies throughout the world

First published 2000

British Library Cataloguing in Publication Data
A catalogue entry for this title is available from the British Library

ISBN 0-582-38156-8

Printed in Great Britain by Ashford Colour Press Ltd, Gosport, Hampshire

Guidance and advice

Schools are now asked to set regular homework. Government guidelines for Year 5 (ages 9–10) suggest 30 minutes of homework a day. Children are also encouraged to do at least 10–20 minutes of reading.

Experimental and investigative science

The aim of the National Curriculum for science is to develop children's knowledge of scientific ideas, processes and skills, and relate these to everyday experiences. Teachers provide opportunities for children to make predictions, plan experiments, learn how to make their test fair, record results, consider evidence, and then think about their results and the effectiveness of the experiment.

All the activities in this book are written to complement the National Curriculum. The emphasis is on short, enjoyable activities designed to stimulate a child's interest in science. Each activity will take 10–20 minutes, depending on the topic, and the amount of drawing and colouring.

Themes and topics

Throughout the book key words have been set in **bold** text – these highlight the themes and content of the activities, and provide a guide to the topics covered.

Encourage your child

Leave your child to do the activity on their own, but be available to answer any questions. Try using phrases like: That's a good idea! How do you think you could do it? What happens if you do it this way? These will encourage your child to think about how they could answer the question for themselves.

If your child is struggling …

Children who need help with reading or writing may need you to work with them. If your child is struggling with the writing, ask them to find the answer and then write it in for them. Remember, even if your child gets stuck, be sure to tell them they are doing well.

The activities start on the next page! Have you got your pens and pencils ready?

Check the answers together

When they have done all they can, sit down with them and go through the answers together. Check they have not misunderstood any important part of the activity. If they have, try to show them why they are going wrong. Ask them to explain what they have done, right or wrong, so that you can understand how they are thinking.

You will find answers to the activities at the back of this book. You can remove the last page if you think your child might look at the answers before trying an activity. Sometimes there is no set answer because your child has been asked for their own ideas. Check that your child's answer is appropriate and shows they have understood the question.

Be positive!

If you think your child needs more help with a particular topic try to think of some similar but easier examples. You don't have to stick to the questions in the book – ask your own: Did you like that? Can you think of any more examples? Have a conversation about the activity. Be positive, giving praise for making an effort and understanding the question, not just getting the right answers. Your child should enjoy doing the activities and at the same time discover that learning is fun.

More on Science

There are many activities you can do outside school that will help develop your child's familiarity with science and provide valuable practice. Make sure your child has plenty of experience of weighing, measuring, observing processes and making comparisons. Look for opportunities to help your child practise predicting what will happen, collecting evidence and recording results. The more practice your child gets the more comfortable with science they will become.

What is a fruit?

The casing is often designed to help the seeds spread away from the parent plant.

When seeds are formed by a plant they are often contained in a casing. The seeds together with their casing are called a **fruit**.

1 Which of the following are fruit? Put a tick beside each fruit.

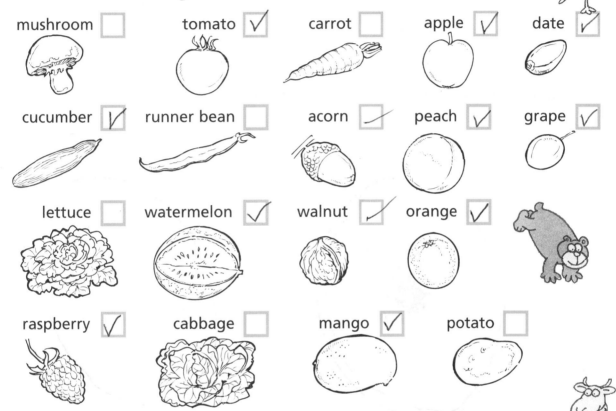

mushroom ☐ tomato ✓ carrot ☐ apple ✓ date ✓

cucumber ✓ runner bean ☐ acorn ✓ peach ✓ grape ✓

lettuce ☐ watermelon ✓ walnut ✓ orange ✓

raspberry ✓ cabbage ☐ mango ✓ potato ☐

2 Look at the fruits above. You eat the seeds of some of these fruits, but not of others. Fill in this table to show which fruits belong to which group.

Eat seeds	Don't eat seeds
Grape	apple
Rasberry	date
	Peach
	Watermelon
	Orange
	Mango

Fruity insides

If you look inside a
fruit you will see
different parts.

skin ——————— seed

flesh or pulp ——————

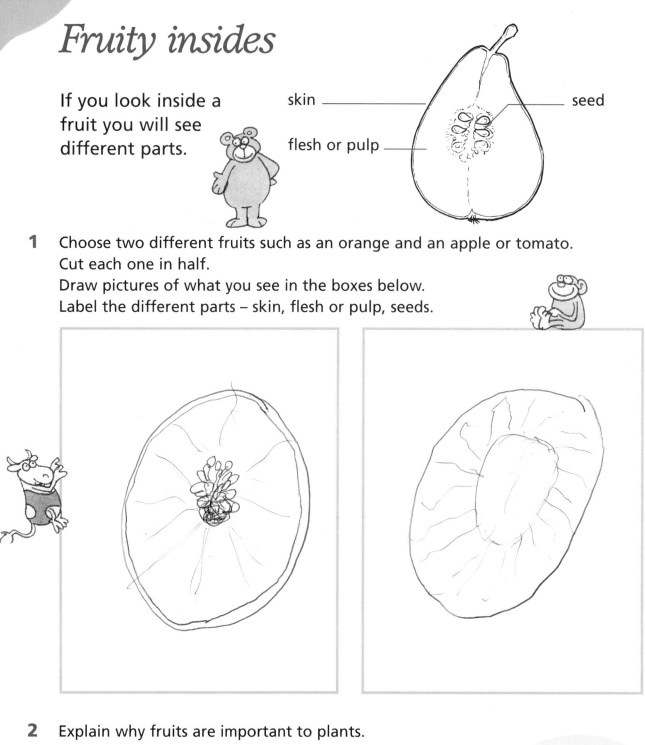

1 Choose two different fruits such as an orange and an apple or tomato.
Cut each one in half.
Draw pictures of what you see in the boxes below.
Label the different parts – skin, flesh or pulp, seeds.

2 Explain why fruits are important to plants.

_____

_____

_____

*Many seeds
have to travel a
long way from the
parent plant.*

3 Why do some fruits have a fleshy pulp
around the seeds?

_____

_____

_____

*We don't eat
the seeds of some
fruits, but other
animals do!*

Sorting fruit

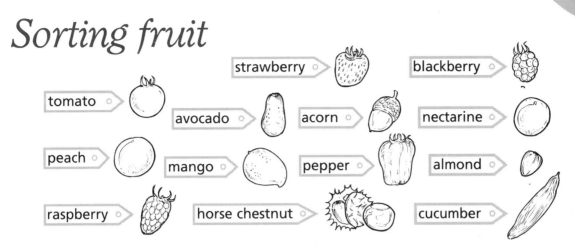

strawberry
blackberry
tomato
avocado
acorn
nectarine
peach
mango
pepper
almond
raspberry
horse chestnut
cucumber

1 Use the **identification key** to sort the fruit into the correct box.

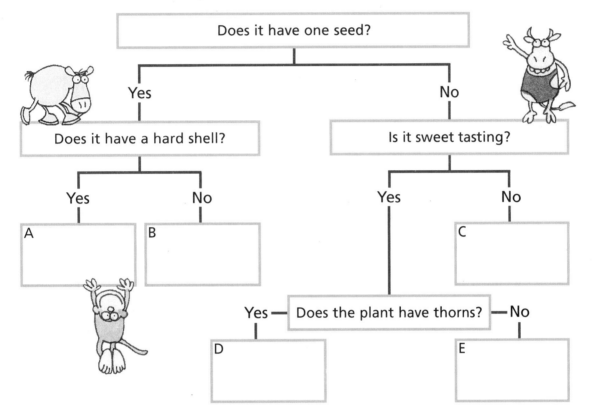

Does it have one seed?

Yes | No

Does it have a hard shell? | Is it sweet tasting?

Yes | No | Yes | No

A | B | | C

Does the plant have thorns?

Yes | No

D | E

2 Now make up your own identification key for sorting the fruit.

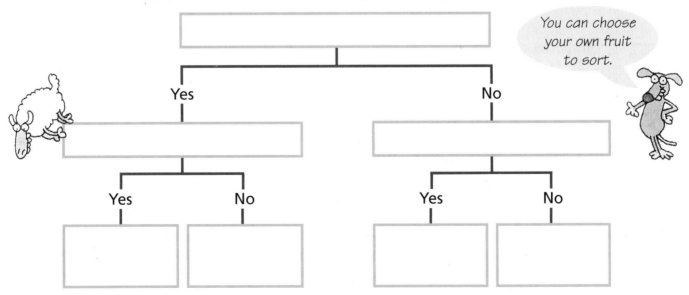

You can choose your own fruit to sort.

Yes | No

Yes | No | Yes | No

Scattering seeds

Fruits and seeds are designed to be able to move a long way from their parent plants.

This is so that they can have more space to grow in and more sunlight and water.

Plants **scatter** or **disperse** their seeds away from their parent plant in different ways.

1 Draw a line to join each type of seed dispersal to the correct description.

Some seeds have 'parachutes' or 'propellers' to help them fly in the wind.

Animals like to eat the fleshy pulp around some seeds.

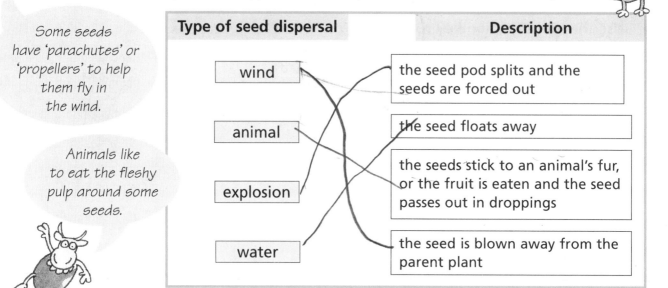

Type of seed dispersal	Description
wind	the seed pod splits and the seeds are forced out
animal	the seed floats away
explosion	the seeds stick to an animal's fur, or the fruit is eaten and the seed passes out in droppings
water	the seed is blown away from the parent plant

2 Look at the shape of these seeds. How do you think the design of the seed helps it to be dispersed? Write down your ideas.

Seed	Type of dispersal	How I think the seed design helps it to be dispersed
Dandelion	Animal	an animal I gets pulled out by
Burdock	Wind	I think that berdock gets blown round becos is so small and it will get blown easyli
Lupin	Water	Lupin would get eaten down by water because altho it is big it cooks very delecate
Coconut	Explosion	a coconut would come down in a explosion because it is very tihty on the tree.

Some seeds are packed tightly inside a hollow casing which explodes when it is ripe.

The casings of some seeds are designed to float on water.

3   Now look at these seeds. Using what you have found out so far decide how they are dispersed. Write your answer underneath each picture.

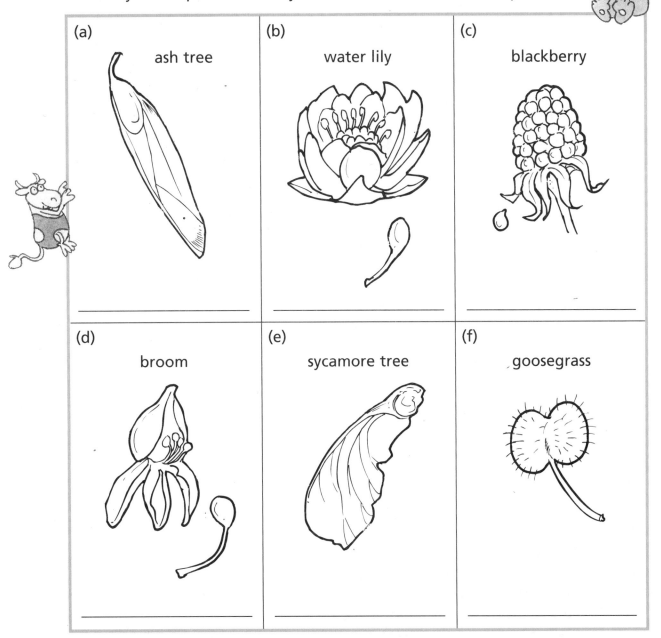

(a) ash tree

(b) water lily

(c) blackberry

(d) broom

(e) sycamore tree

(f) goosegrass

4   Give two reasons why seeds need to be dispersed.

_____

_____

_____

_____

_____

From a seed to a plant

Germination is when a seed starts to grow. A **root** and a **shoot** are produced.

These activities are fun to do and you can see how a plant starts to grow.

Investigating butterbeans

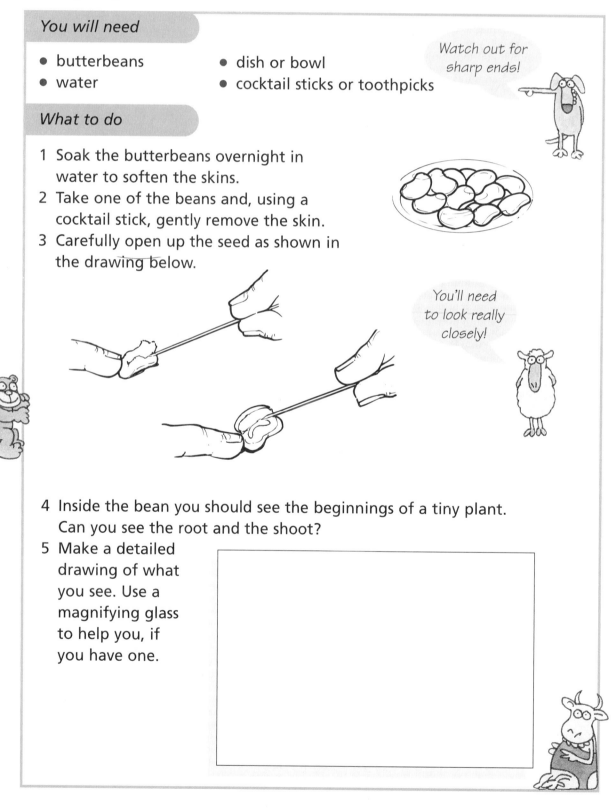

You will need

- butterbeans
- water
- dish or bowl
- cocktail sticks or toothpicks

Watch out for sharp ends!

What to do

1 Soak the butterbeans overnight in water to soften the skins.
2 Take one of the beans and, using a cocktail stick, gently remove the skin.
3 Carefully open up the seed as shown in the drawing below.

You'll need to look really closely!

4 Inside the bean you should see the beginnings of a tiny plant. Can you see the root and the shoot?
5 Make a detailed drawing of what you see. Use a magnifying glass to help you, if you have one.

Flower explosion

If you take a flower to pieces you will be able to see all the different parts that are inside.

Ask an adult if you can have a flower to use. A poppy, daffodil or tulip would be good.

You may need to cut through some parts – do this with an adult.

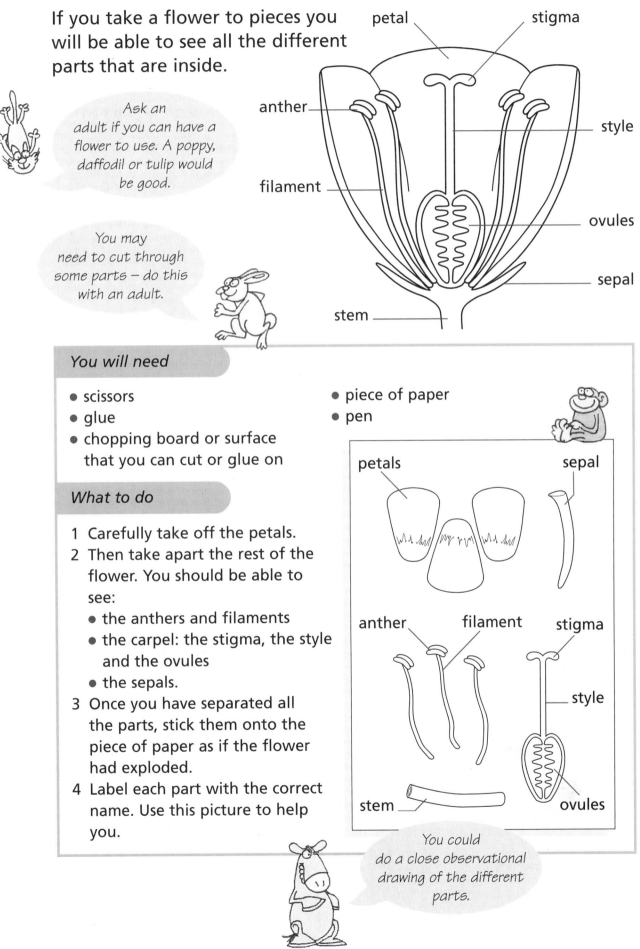

You will need

- scissors
- glue
- chopping board or surface that you can cut or glue on
- piece of paper
- pen

What to do

1. Carefully take off the petals.
2. Then take apart the rest of the flower. You should be able to see:
   - the anthers and filaments
   - the carpel: the stigma, the style and the ovules
   - the sepals.
3. Once you have separated all the parts, stick them onto the piece of paper as if the flower had exploded.
4. Label each part with the correct name. Use this picture to help you.

You could do a close observational drawing of the different parts.

Flower power

Make your own model of a flower.

Ask an adult to help you with the cutting.

You will need

- a piece of plain paper
- scissors
- glue
- colouring pencils or felt-tip pens

What to do

1 Trace the drawings of the outside of the flower and the outside of the carpel onto the sheet of plain paper.

2 Colour in the parts, then cut them out.

3 Colour in the inside of the flower and the inside of the carpel on page 13. Stick the tracing of the outside of the carpel on top of the inside of the carpel in the drawing on page 13.

4 Stick the tracing of the outside of the flower on top of the inside of the flower in the drawing on page 13.

Don't cut off the tabs! You'll need them to stick the flower parts together.

Put glue only on the tabs! The tabs act as a hinge so that you can open up your flower to see the inside.

12

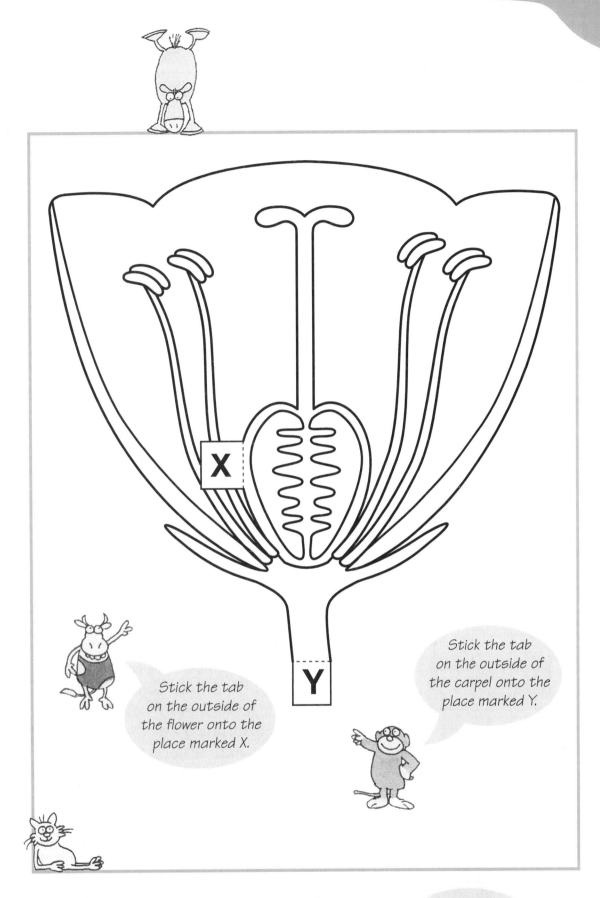

1 Draw these parts on the inside of your flower.

- extra stamens
- seeds in the ovary

An anther and a filament together are called a stamen.

2 Draw an insect flying to your flower to pollinate it.

Parts of a flower

Use the clues to find the missing **parts** of a flower.

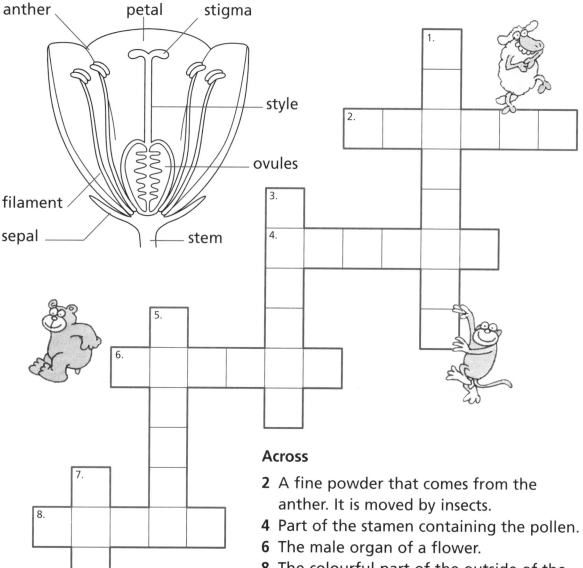

Across

2 A fine powder that comes from the anther. It is moved by insects.
4 Part of the stamen containing the pollen.
6 The male organ of a flower.
8 The colourful part of the outside of the flower which attracts the insects.
9 The female organ containing the egg cells.

Down

1 Part of the stamen which supports the anther.
3 The female organ which contains the stigma, style and ovary.
5 Part of the carpel which the pollen lands on.
7 Leaf-like parts at the bottom of the flower which protects the flower when it's growing.

Pollination

The boxes and sentences below explain how the flower helps the plant to **reproduce**. This is called **pollination**.

1 Put the boxes in the right order, 1 to 5, by writing the correct number in the box.

*But they are in the **wrong** order!*

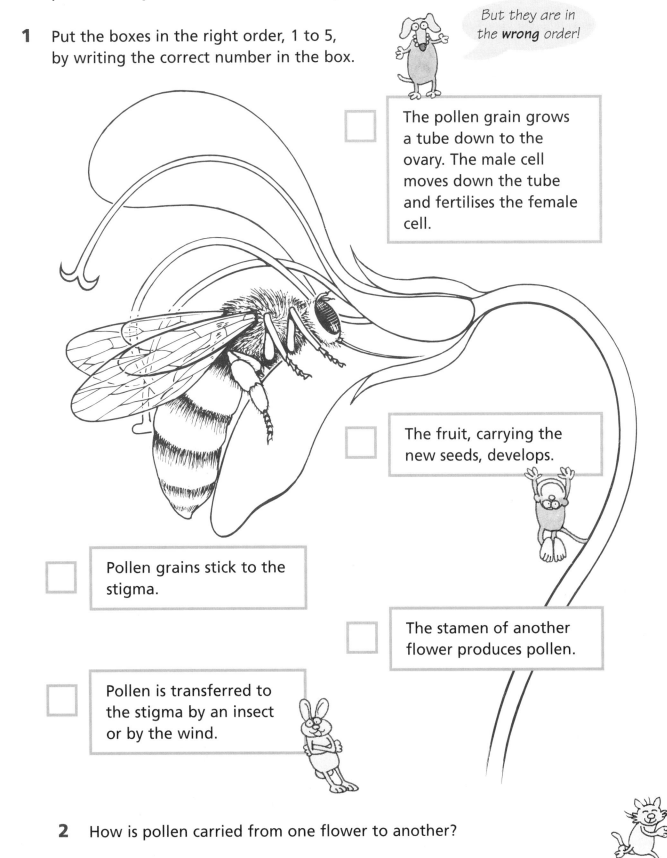

The pollen grain grows a tube down to the ovary. The male cell moves down the tube and fertilises the female cell.

The fruit, carrying the new seeds, develops.

Pollen grains stick to the stigma.

The stamen of another flower produces pollen.

Pollen is transferred to the stigma by an insect or by the wind.

2 How is pollen carried from one flower to another?

_____

Plant life cycle

The pictures and sentences below describe the **life cycle** of the dandelion, but they are in the wrong order.

1   Match each sentence to the correct picture by drawing a line.

2   Number the pictures to give the correct order.

Number 1 is done for you.

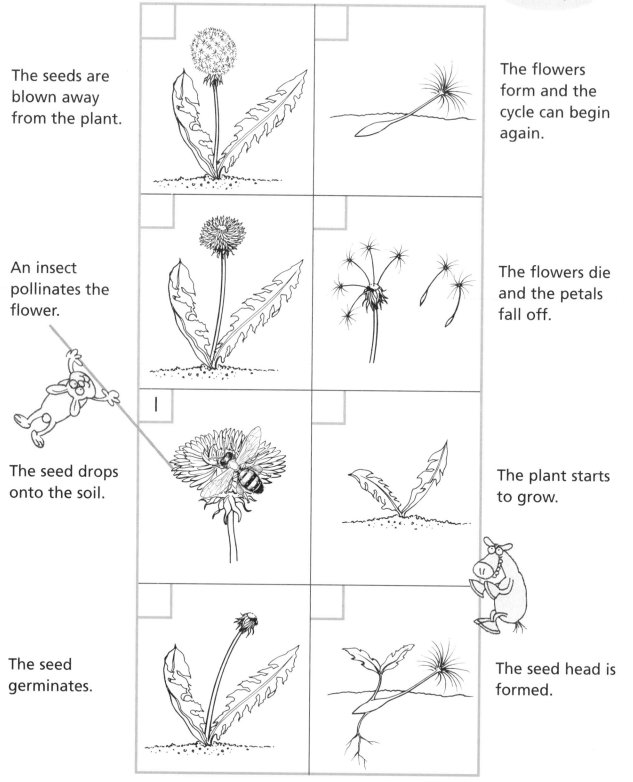

The seeds are blown away from the plant.

The flowers form and the cycle can begin again.

An insect pollinates the flower.

The flowers die and the petals fall off.

The seed drops onto the soil.

The plant starts to grow.

The seed germinates.

The seed head is formed.

16

Word wizard

Like all living things, plants have a **life cycle**. How much can you remember about the life cycle of a plant?

1 Read the definitions below and find the correct word in the word search. Draw a ring around each word.

2 Write the word in the correct position in the grid below the word search.

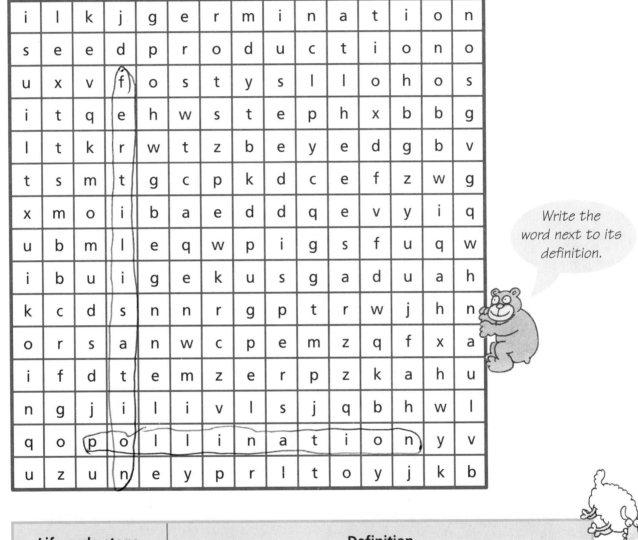

i	l	k	j	g	e	r	m	i	n	a	t	i	o	n
s	e	e	d	p	r	o	d	u	c	t	i	o	n	o
u	x	v	f	o	s	t	y	s	l	l	o	h	o	s
i	t	q	e	h	w	s	t	e	p	h	x	b	b	g
l	t	k	r	w	t	z	b	e	y	e	d	g	b	v
t	s	m	t	g	c	p	k	d	c	e	f	z	w	g
x	m	o	i	b	a	e	d	d	q	e	v	y	i	q
u	b	m	l	e	q	w	p	i	g	s	f	u	q	w
i	b	u	i	g	e	k	u	s	g	a	d	u	a	h
k	c	d	s	n	n	r	g	p	t	r	w	j	h	n
o	r	s	a	n	w	c	p	e	m	z	q	f	x	a
i	f	d	t	e	m	z	e	r	p	z	k	a	h	u
n	g	j	i	l	i	v	l	s	j	q	b	h	w	l
q	o	p	o	l	l	i	n	a	t	i	o	n	y	v
u	z	u	n	e	y	p	r	l	t	o	y	j	k	b

Write the word next to its definition.

Life cycle stage	Definition
Fertalisation	the start of a plant's life when it sprouts and comes to life
polonation	when pollen from another flower is placed on the stigma
	when a male cell joins with a female cell in the carpel
	when a seed is formed
	when seeds are moved away from their parent plant

Animal life cycles

Some animals completely change their shape and form as they grow into adults.

The pictures below show some of the stages in the **life cycles** of the fly and the frog.

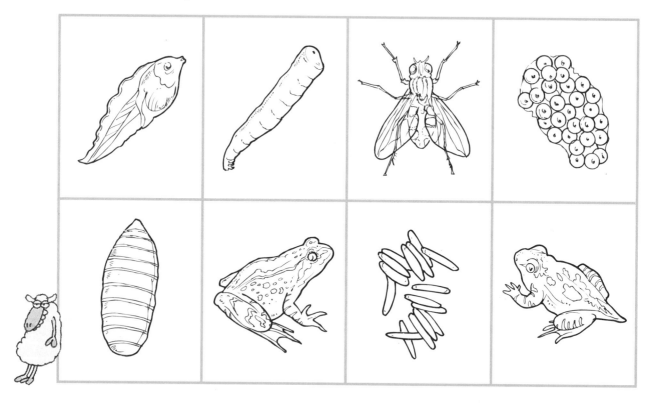

1   Draw each of the pictures in the correct positions in the circles on the opposite page.

Draw your pictures in the segments with the thick outlines.

2   Choose the correct sentence to explain each stage of the cycle. Write the sentence next to the picture you have drawn.

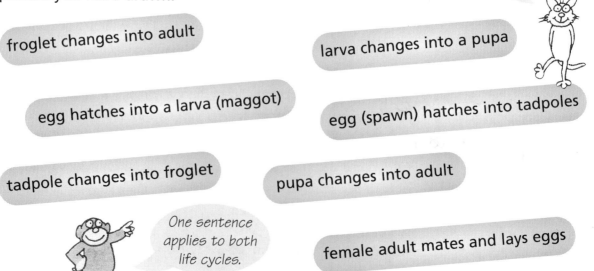

froglet changes into adult

larva changes into a pupa

egg hatches into a larva (maggot)

egg (spawn) hatches into tadpoles

tadpole changes into froglet

pupa changes into adult

One sentence applies to both life cycles.

female adult mates and lays eggs

Life cycle of a fly

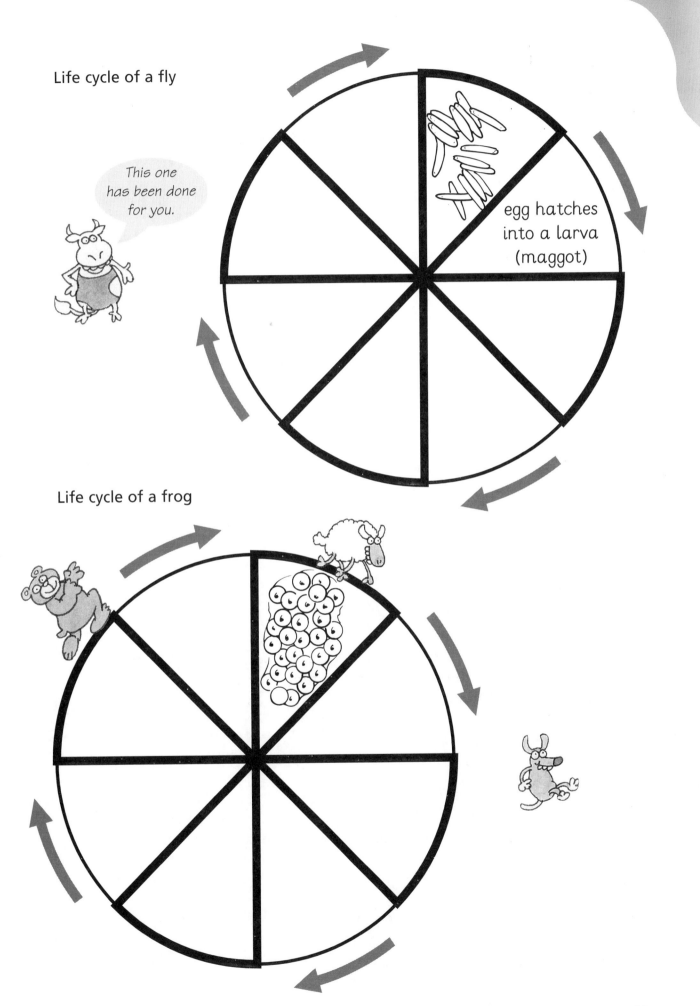

This one has been done for you.

egg hatches into a larva (maggot)

Life cycle of a frog

19

Human life cycle

Humans are **mammals**. When they are born, mammals are small copies of their parents.

1 Below are pictures illustrating the **human life cycle**. Put the pictures in the correct order by numbering them from 1 to 6.

Start with 1 for the earliest stage of the life cycle.

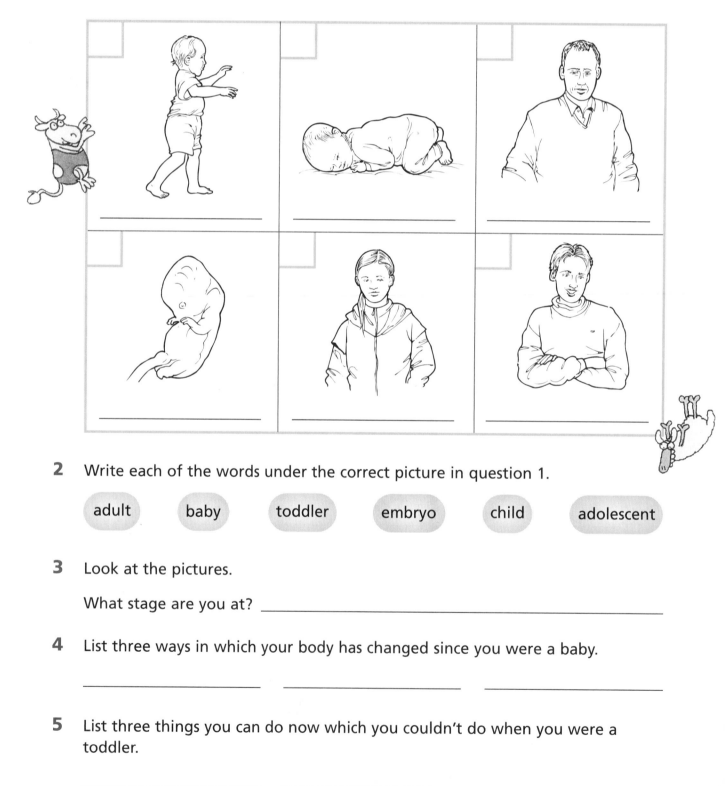

2 Write each of the words under the correct picture in question 1.

adult   baby   toddler   embryo   child   adolescent

3 Look at the pictures.

What stage are you at? _____

4 List three ways in which your body has changed since you were a baby.

_____   _____   _____

5 List three things you can do now which you couldn't do when you were a toddler.

_____   _____   _____

6 List two similarities between the life cycle of the frog and the human life cycle.

_____

_____

7 List two differences between the life cycle of the frog and the human life cycle.

_____

_____

8 Research a life cycle of your own.

Use page 19 to help you.

Life cycle of a _____

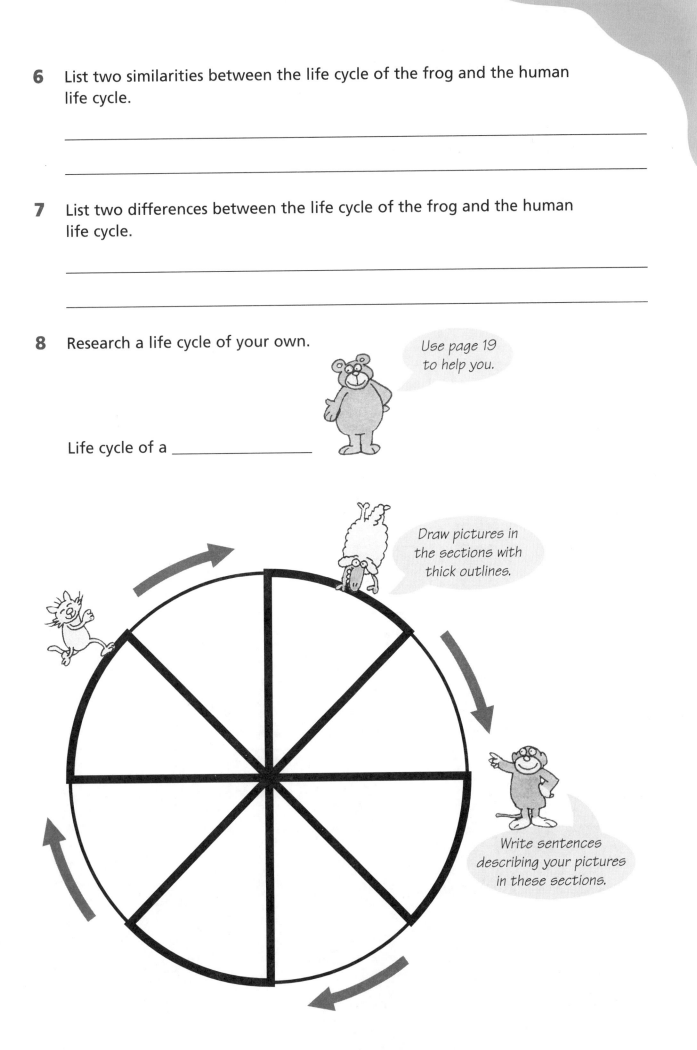

Draw pictures in the sections with thick outlines.

Write sentences describing your pictures in these sections.

Food and health

Food provides **energy** and **nutrients** to help you grow and stay healthy.

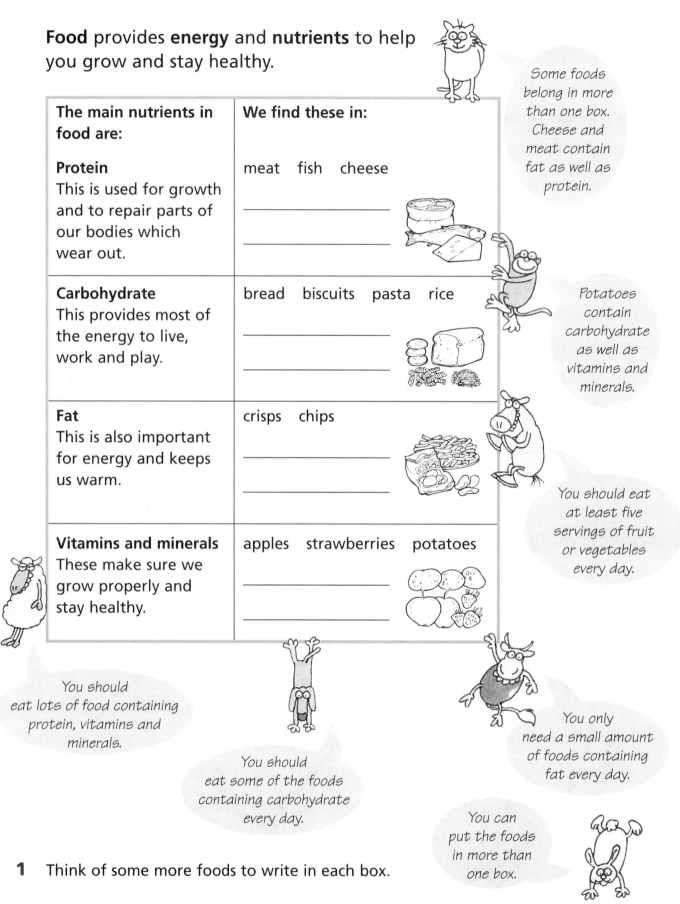

Some foods belong in more than one box. Cheese and meat contain fat as well as protein.

The main nutrients in food are:	We find these in:
Protein This is used for growth and to repair parts of our bodies which wear out.	meat fish cheese _____ _____
Carbohydrate This provides most of the energy to live, work and play.	bread biscuits pasta rice _____ _____
Fat This is also important for energy and keeps us warm.	crisps chips _____ _____
Vitamins and minerals These make sure we grow properly and stay healthy.	apples strawberries potatoes _____ _____

Potatoes contain carbohydrate as well as vitamins and minerals.

You should eat at least five servings of fruit or vegetables every day.

You should eat lots of food containing protein, vitamins and minerals.

You should eat some of the foods containing carbohydrate every day.

You only need a small amount of foods containing fat every day.

You can put the foods in more than one box.

1   Think of some more foods to write in each box.

A healthy diet must be **balanced** which means we need to eat food from each group in our meals.

2 Keep a record of the foods you eat in one day.
Write them down in the correct boxes.

Food group	Breakfast	Lunch	Dinner	Snacks
Protein				
Carbohydrate				
Fat				
Vitamins and minerals				

3 Do you think your day's food is balanced?

_____

4 Why? _____

5 Plan a day's menu which is balanced.

| Breakfast |
| Lunch |
| Dinner |
| Snacks |

Remember to check that you have included five pieces of fruit or vegetables during the day.

Try to plan a balanced meal for a vegetarian.

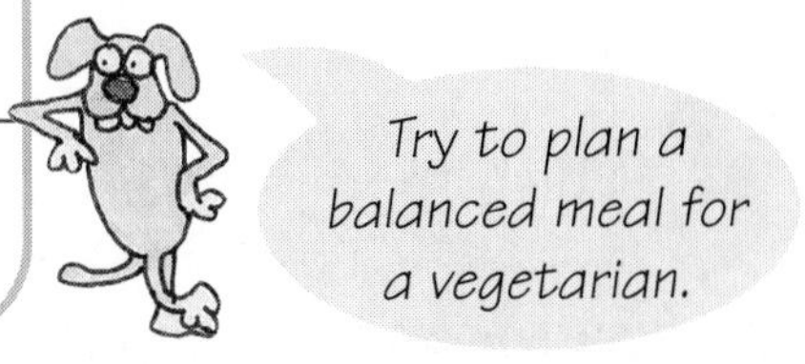

You are what you eat

This label comes from a box of cornflakes. You can find labels like this on all food packaging. It tells you what the food contains.

Nutrition Information per 100g	
Energy	1560 kJ 367 kcal
Protein	7.3 g
Carbohydrate	82.7 g
Fat	0.8 g
Sodium	1.1 g
Fibre	3.6 g
Vitamins	
Vitamin C	35 mg
Niacin	18.0 mg
Vitamin B6	2.0 mg
Riboflavin	1.6 mg
Thiamin	1.4 mg
Folic Acid	400.0 mg
Vitamin D	5.0 mg
Vitamin B12	1.0 mg
Iron	14.0 mg

Energy is measured in kilojoules or kilocalories.

We write this as kJ or kcal.

Our bodies need **energy** all the time, for breathing, running, sleeping and working.
Food provides our bodies with the energy it needs.

Write what you find in the table.

1   Look at the food label from the cornflakes box.

How much energy is in 100 g of cornflakes? _____

2   Find some other labels on packets of food.
Write down how much energy is in 100 g of each food.

Type of food	Amount of energy in 100 g of the food

3   Which food provides the most energy? _____

4   Which food provides the least energy? _____

Claire found the **energy content** of some foods. She recorded the information in this table.

If you play or work hard then you need more energy and you may eat more food.

Energy content			
Food	**kcal**	**Food**	**kcal**
small carton of orange juice	70	1 apple	50
		1 slice of bread	70
1 packet of crisps	130	1 glass of milk	130
1 plain biscuit	30		

She then found out how much energy she would need to do different activities. These are her results.

But if you don't use up the energy then it is stored in your body as fat and you may become overweight.

Activity	Energy needed
4 minutes of jogging or 8 minutes of swimming	50 kcal
10 minutes of walking or 8 minutes of playing football	70 kcal
10 minutes of cycling or $1\frac{1}{2}$ hours of sleep	80 kcal
10 minutes of dance or $1\frac{1}{4}$ hours of watching television	100 kcal

5   Use the information from the above tables to fill in the spaces below. Then decide what food to eat to get exactly the right amount of energy.

Activity	Time	kcal	Food
dance	10 mins		
football		140	
cycle		320	
sleep	3 hours		
swim	24 mins		

The pulse

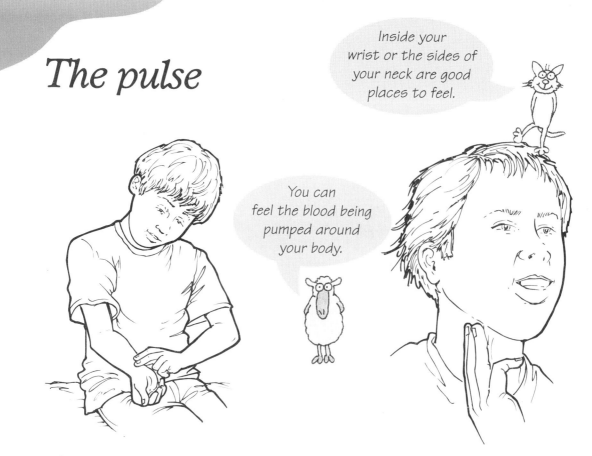

When you can feel your heart pumping blood around your body you have found your **pulse**. It throbs each time your heart beats.

1 Sit still for two minutes then feel for your pulse.

When you have found it, count how many times it pulses in one minute. This will be your **pulse rate**.

Your pulse rate tells you the number of times that your heart beats in one minute.

My pulse rate is _____.

In order to check how accurate your measurement was, repeat your pulse reading twice more. For example:

1st reading	2nd reading	3rd reading
87 beats per minute	85 beats per minute	86 beats per minute

2 If your three readings are different, which one will you use, and why?

_____

Exercise those muscles

When you are running, jumping or even walking quickly you need more energy so your heart beats faster. Your heart sends blood around your body carrying food and oxygen to the parts that need energy.

Your body uses oxygen to burn food to provide energy.

Carry out these activities to see what happens to your body after **exercising**. Carry out each activity for 2 minutes, then measure your pulse after each activity.

You will need a stop watch.

Activity		Pulse
resting		
touching toes		
skipping		
jogging on the spot		

1 Which activity made your pulse rate go the highest? _____

Why do you think this is? _____

2 Find the difference between your resting pulse and your pulse after

skipping. _____

3 Think about what happens to your body during exercise. Look at the statements below and tick the ones you think are true.

Exercise is hard work, but now I feel much fitter!

blood is pumped slower ☐	get hotter ☐	feel cold ☐
breathing slows down ☐	muscles relax ☐	feel hot ☐
heart beats faster ☐	feel sweaty ☐	feel tired ☐
breathing speeds up ☐	blood is pumped quicker ☐	
heart beat slows down ☐	muscles work harder ☐	

Different pulse rates

Here is a list of **pulse rate**s taken after different activities.

1 Match the pulse rate to the correct activity.

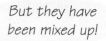
But they have been mixed up!

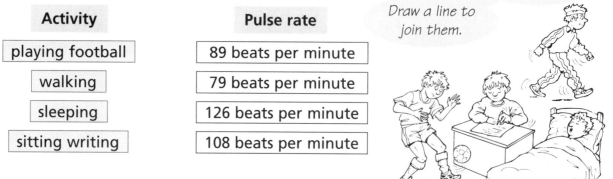

Activity	Pulse rate
playing football	89 beats per minute
walking	79 beats per minute
sleeping	126 beats per minute
sitting writing	108 beats per minute

Draw a line to join them.

Fair testing

Class 5W wanted to find out what happened to the pulse rate after walking, jogging slowly, skipping and running. They measured their pulse rate after 2 minutes of each activity. Then they stopped the activity and rested for another 2 minutes, and measured their pulse rate again.

2 Make a list of the things they needed to do to make sure it was a **fair test**.

_____   _____

_____   _____

Here is a graph of the results from one of their tests.

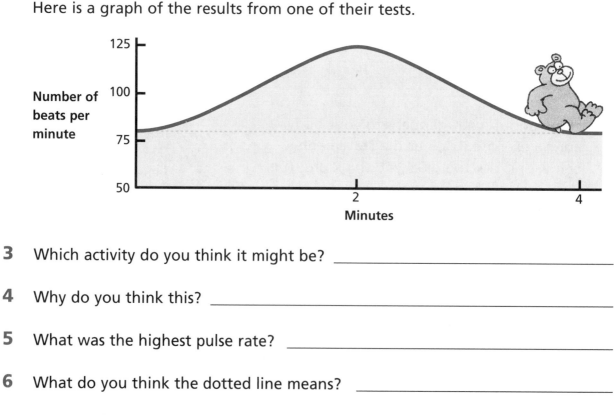

3 Which activity do you think it might be? _____

4 Why do you think this? _____

5 What was the highest pulse rate? _____

6 What do you think the dotted line means? _____

Have a heart

Your **heart** is a **muscle** which pumps blood around your body. This is what happens:

Your blood 'picks up' the oxygen from your lungs and then it travels into your heart. The heart pumps or pushes the blood around your body. It travels through your arteries and goes to every part of your body so your muscles and organs can use the food and oxygen to make them work. Veins carry the blood back to your heart so the blood can be pumped back to your lungs again to 'pick up' more oxygen.

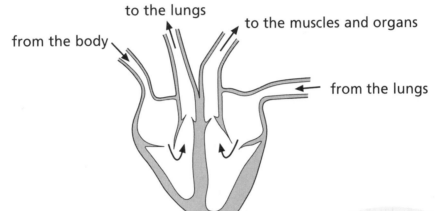

to the lungs

to the muscles and organs

from the body

from the lungs

The labels and the direction of the arrows will help you.

1 Colour red the part of the heart which carries the blood containing the most oxygen.

2 Colour blue the part of the heart which carries the blood containing least oxygen.

3 These phrases have been put in the wrong order. Put them in the correct order using the information above to help you.

Write numbers in the boxes to show the correct order.

	The blood with little oxygen is carried
I	The heart pumps the blood to the lungs
	Then blood with oxygen travels away from the heart
	it is pumped back to the lungs so
	back to the heart in veins, and then
	more oxygen can be 'picked up'.
	through arteries to the muscles and organs.
	where the oxygen is 'picked up'.

The first phrase has been done for you – what comes next?

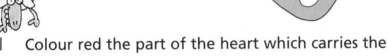

Muscles and skeletons

A **skeleton** is a framework of bones in an animal. The skeleton is important to humans for three reasons:

- so the body can keep its shape
- to protect and support important organs
- so **muscles** can be attached.

A **joint** is where two bones join.
Here are some of the important joints.

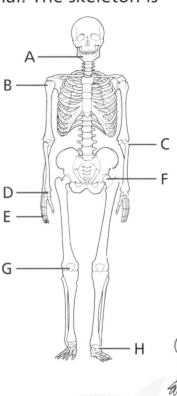

	jaw		ankle
	elbow		knuckles
	knee		shoulder
	wrist		hip

1 Colour these joints on the skeleton and write the letters in the correct boxes.

Bones cannot move on their own, so muscles are attached to them. Muscles can **contract** or **relax**. They mostly work in pairs so when one muscle is relaxed the other is contracted.

When a muscle relaxes it becomes long and thin.

When a muscle contracts it becomes shorter and fatter.

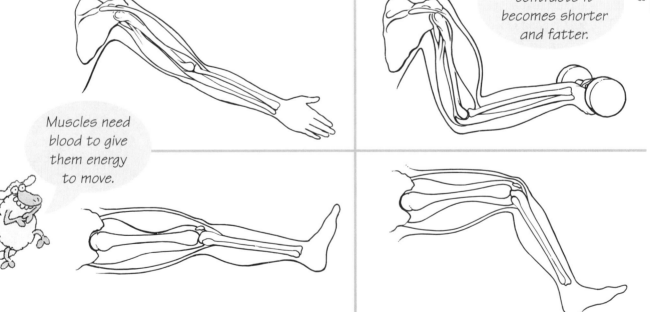

Muscles need blood to give them energy to move.

2 In each picture colour the contracted muscle red and the relaxed muscle blue.

Keeping healthy

It is important to keep your body **healthy**.

1   Draw a ring around the things in this picture which are unhealthy.

Look at this picture carefully. There are lots of things in the picture which are *unhealthy*.

2   Choose four things that you have put a ring around and explain why they are unhealthy.

_____

_____

_____

_____

Healthy poster

You have been asked by the local nurse to design a poster to be displayed in the doctor's surgery.

Choose one of the topics below and create an eye-catching poster which can be seen from some distance away.

- the dangers of smoking
- the dangers of taking drugs
- the dangers of taking other people's medicine
- the importance of visiting the dentist regularly and keeping your teeth clean
- the importance of regular exercise
- the importance of washing your hands after you have been to the toilet

Think carefully about words to go on the poster.

People who look at it need to understand what it is about without an explanation.

Day and night

It is **daytime** in the parts of the Earth that are facing the Sun so the light shines on them.

It is **night-time** in the parts of the Earth that are facing away from the Sun so that they are in shadow.

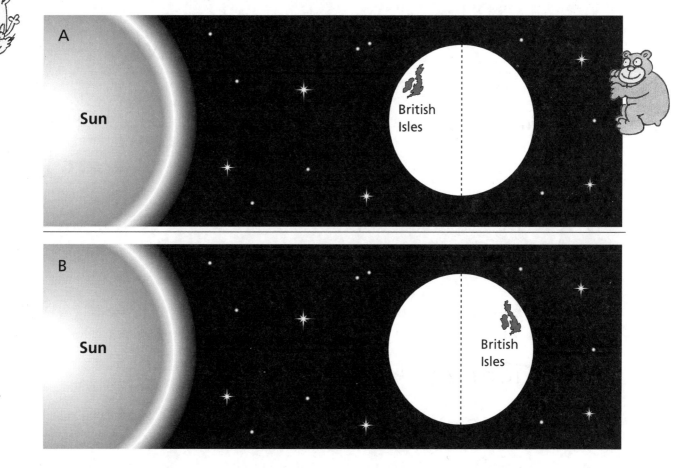

1 On both pictures colour in grey the part of the Earth where it is night. Colour in yellow the part of the Earth where it is day.

2 Which picture shows the British Isles having night?   B

   Which picture shows the British Isles having day? A

3 Explain in your own words how the place where you live has day and night.

These words might help you.

| 24 hours   rotate   axis   shadow |
| shines   Earth   Sun |

_____

_____

_____

Spheres in space

Here are some facts about the **Earth**, **Sun** and **Moon**.

Don't worry about the blank parts. You will be filling those in later.

	Diameter in km	Circumference in km	Shape	What is it?	What is it made of?
Earth	12,760	40,090	sphere	Land	?
Sun	1,390,000	4,367,000	spere	Gass	Gas
Moon	3,476	10,920	sfere	crater	rock

1 Look at the following list of objects:

pea   beachball   tennis ball

The proper name for a ball shape is a *sphere*.

Which of these objects would you choose to represent the Earth, Sun and Moon?

Earth Tennis ball

Sun Beach ball

Moon pea .

2 Now fill in the shape of the Earth, Sun and Moon in the chart.

The Sun is almost exactly 400 times bigger than the Moon.

But by coincidence the Sun is also 400 times further away.

This means that during a total eclipse the Moon exactly covers the Sun!

Draw a line to join each shape to the correct picture.

3 Match the words and phrases below to their correct partners, A, B or C.

Earth

orbits Earth

a burning ball which gives out light

made of rock and metal

Sun

made of rock and metal

planet

star

satellite

orbits the Sun

Moon

made of gas

A

B

C

4 Now fill in the rest of the gaps in the chart on page 34.

Orbits

An **orbit** is a curved path that a moving object takes.

The planets in our **solar system** orbit the Sun, taking an oval path.

The oval path is called an ellipse.

1 Label the boxes correctly on the picture below.

The Sun	The Earth	The Moon

Key
- the Earth orbits the Sun
- the Moon orbits the Earth

The Sun

The Erthe

The moon

2 Colour the Earth's orbit around the Sun in red.
Colour the Moon's orbit around the Earth in blue.

3 It takes the Earth a year to orbit the Sun.

How many days is this? _365 days._

4 It takes the Moon 28 days to orbit the Earth.
A year is divided up into parts which are about 28 days long.

What are these parts called? _____

Lunar puzzle

The Moon's appearance changes over 28 days.

The different shapes we see are called the **phases of the Moon**.

Full Moon   half   crescent   New Moon

Use the diagrams above to help you.

Crossword answers filled in:

1. FULL
2. SUN
3. MOON
4. PHASES
5. CRESCENT
6. MAN
7. SHADOW
8. NEW
9. ORBIT
10.

Find the answers to these clues.

1. When the Moon's face is completely lit up.
2. The Moon is lit up by this.
3. This orbits the Earth every 28 days.
4. The changes in what we see of the Moon are called ____ Phases
5. This is the phase before a New Moon.
6. Neil Armstrong was the first ____ man ____ on the Moon.
7. If we can see only half of the Moon the rest is in ____ Shadow.
8. If we can't see any light reflected it is a ____ New ____ Moon.
9. Every 28 days the Moon makes an ____ orbit ____ of the Earth.
10. The Moon is not made of this!

If you completed this puzzle correctly, you should be able to read two words in the shaded boxes. Write them here.

_____   _____

How long is this?

Sunrise, sunset

Here is a chart showing the approximate GMT times of **sunrise** and **sunset** in Birmingham throughout the year. Look carefully at the information and then answer the questions below.

Months	Sunrise	Sunset	Length of day in hours
January	08:30	17:30	9
February	07:45	18:15	$10\frac{1}{2}$
March	07:00	19:00	12
April	06:15	19:45	$13\frac{1}{2}$
May	05:30	20:30	15
June	04:45	21:15	$16\frac{1}{2}$
July	05:30	20:30	
August	06:15	19:45	
September	07:00	19:00	
October	07:45	18:15	
November	08:30	17:30	
December	09:15	16:45	

This table uses the 24-hour clock.

Seven o'clock in the morning is written 07:00.

Seven o'clock in the evening is written 19:00.

Half past twelve is written 12:30.

1   Calculate the length of the day in hours for these months:

     July   August   September   October   November   December

    _____   _____   _____   _____   _____   _____

2   (a) What time does the Sun rise in January?   _____

     (b) What time does the Sun set in June?   _____

3   (a) What time does the Sun set in December?_____

     (b) What time does the Sun set in July?   _____

4 Use the information in the table on page 38 to fill in the bar chart to show the missing hours of daylight for June to December.

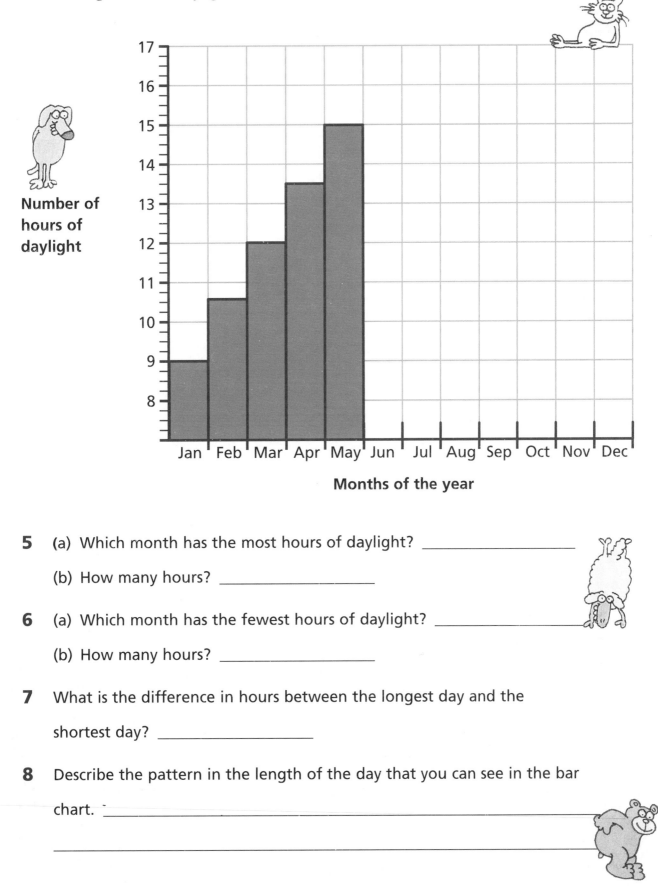

Number of hours of daylight

Months of the year

5 (a) Which month has the most hours of daylight? _____

(b) How many hours? _____

6 (a) Which month has the fewest hours of daylight? _____

(b) How many hours? _____

7 What is the difference in hours between the longest day and the

shortest day? _____

8 Describe the pattern in the length of the day that you can see in the bar

chart. _____

_____

Space expert

Imagine that you have been asked to write an entry for a new book about **space**. The book is for 7 year olds.

Write three short paragraphs about the Sun, Earth and Moon. Use some of the facts you have found out already. Colour in the spheres to look like the Sun, Earth and Moon.

Magic crystals

Evaporation is when a liquid turns into a gas.

You will need

- salt
- water from the hot tap
- saucer
- cup

What to do

1 Run some hot water from the tap into a cup.
2 Add salt to the water and stir. Keep adding salt and stirring until no more salt will dissolve in the water.
3 Pour some of the salty water into a saucer so that it is 2–3 mm deep.
4 Put the saucer in a warm place, such as on the windowsill.
5 Look to see what has happened after three days.

Hot water can scald you – ask an adult to help you with hot water.

Now answer these questions.

1 What happened to the salty water after you left it in the warm place?

_____

2 What is left in the saucer?

_____

3 What do we call this process?

_____

Vanishing act

Remember, **evaporation** is when a liquid changes into a gas.

When water evaporates, the gas is called water vapour.

1 Underneath each pair of pictures, write a sentence to explain what has happened to the water.

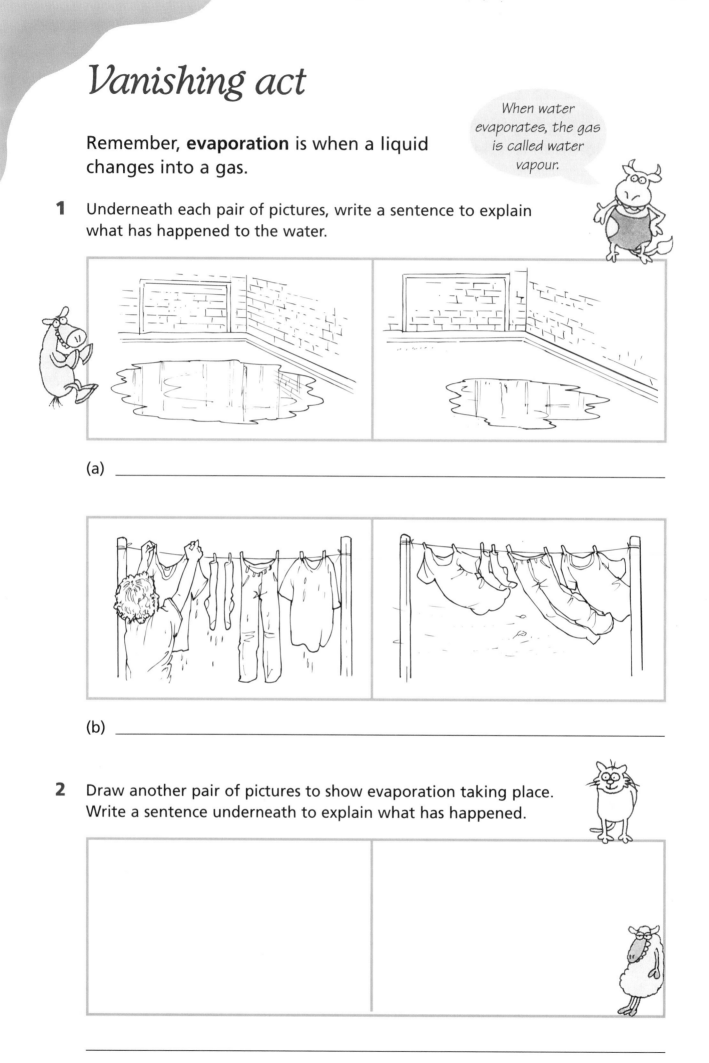

(a) _____

(b) _____

2 Draw another pair of pictures to show evaporation taking place. Write a sentence underneath to explain what has happened.

_____

Investigating evaporation

Does water **evaporate** more quickly in warm places than in cold places?

Don't give up! Think about this a little bit.

1   Use this table to design a fair test to answer the question.

What I want to find out.
What I will use.
What I will do.
How I will make the test fair.
How I will record my observations.

Write about it and draw a diagram.

2   What do you think will happen in the test?

This is your prediction.

Condensation

Condensation is when a gas turns into a liquid.

It was a cold winter's day and Sasha had got wet playing outside. So she decided to have a bath. She filled up the bath with hot water and had a long soak. After she got out she noticed that the mirror was steamed up. When she looked carefully she could see little droplets forming on the surface.

This happened as the warm air in the bathroom met the cold mirror and caused water vapour in the air to form droplets of water on the mirror's surface. This is called condensation.

It was a hot summer's day. Mark had been playing outside and had got very hot and thirsty so he needed a drink. He poured some cold juice straight from the fridge into a glass. When he looked carefully he noticed the glass had steamed up and tiny droplets had formed on the surface of the glass.

1 What was the liquid that was on the mirror and the glass? _____

2 Where have the droplets come from? _____

3 Explain in your own words why the droplets appeared on the surfaces.

_____

_____

4 What is this process called? _____

5 Think of another example of this process.
Write a description and draw a picture in the boxes.

Try to think of something that happens out of doors.

Water, water, everywhere

Water can be found in three **states**: **solid**, **liquid** and **gas**.

1 Write the correct state in the box underneath each picture below.

  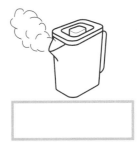

This graph illustrates what happens when a block of ice is heated.
As it gets warmer, the water **changes state**.

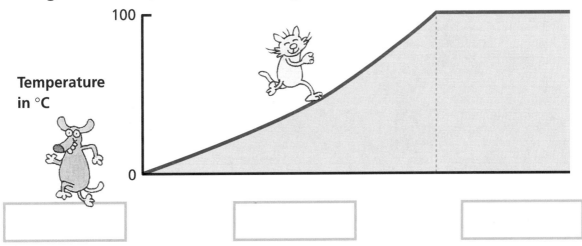

Temperature in °C

2 Write the correct states in the boxes underneath the graph.

Gas	Liquid	Solid

3 At what temperature does water change from a solid to a liquid?

_____

4 At what temperature does water change from a liquid to a gas?

_____

5 At what temperature does water change from a gas to a liquid?

_____

6 At what temperature does water change from a liquid to a solid?

_____

The water cycle

Rainfall is part of a **cycle** where evaporation and condensation take place.

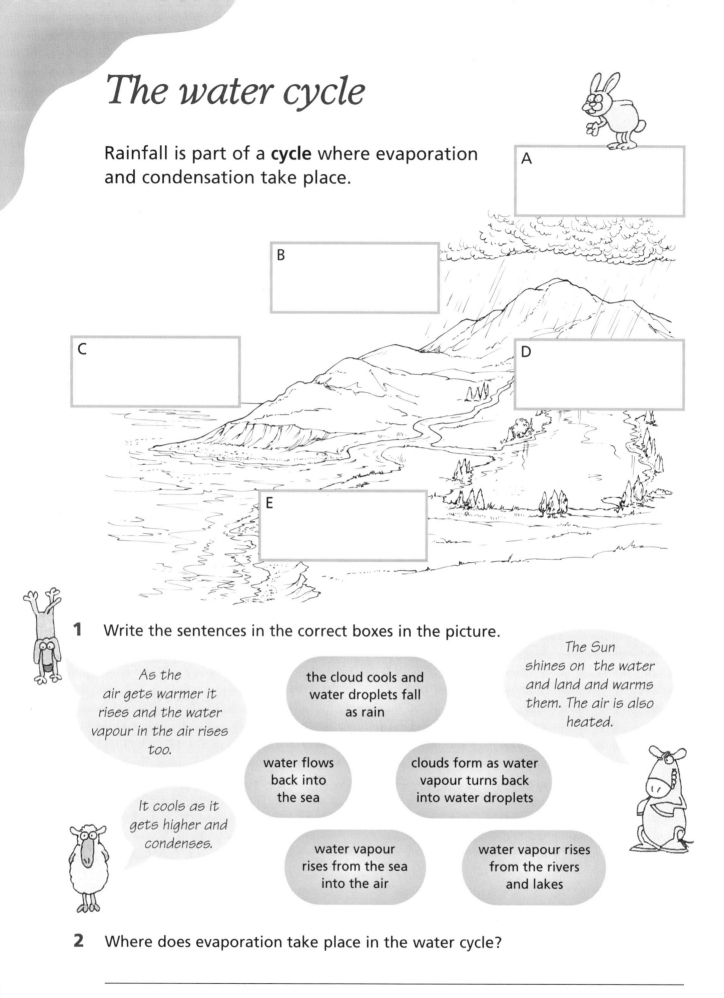

1 Write the sentences in the correct boxes in the picture.

As the air gets warmer it rises and the water vapour in the air rises too.

the cloud cools and water droplets fall as rain

The Sun shines on the water and land and warms them. The air is also heated.

water flows back into the sea

clouds form as water vapour turns back into water droplets

It cools as it gets higher and condenses.

water vapour rises from the sea into the air

water vapour rises from the rivers and lakes

2 Where does evaporation take place in the water cycle?

_____

3 Where does condensation take place in the water cycle?

_____

A model water cycle

Sara and Ali have made a model **water cycle**. Sara poured some warm water into a jar. Ali put some clingfilm over the jar and then placed a bag of ice cubes on to the cling film cover.

ice cubes in a bag

clingfilm

water

When water vapour in the air is cooled, it **condenses** and changes back to water.

Then Sara and Ali placed the model near to a window and observed.

1   This is a diagram of what happened over the next few minutes. Label the diagram, using these words.

| ice | water | condensation | drips |

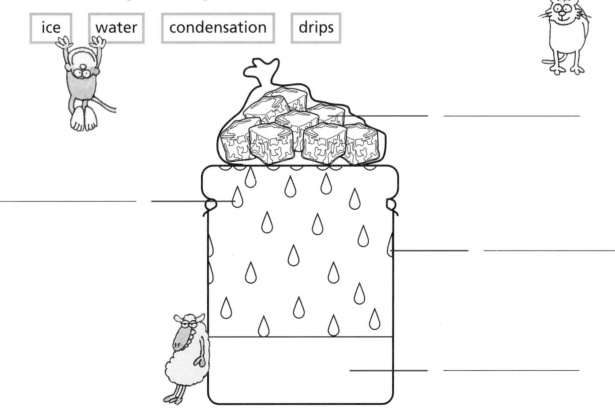

2   Describe what has happened in this experiment.

_____

_____

_____

_____

Real gases

Gases are all around us – but how do we know they are there?
Each of the pictures shows gases at work. Write a sentence
underneath each one to say what the gas is doing.

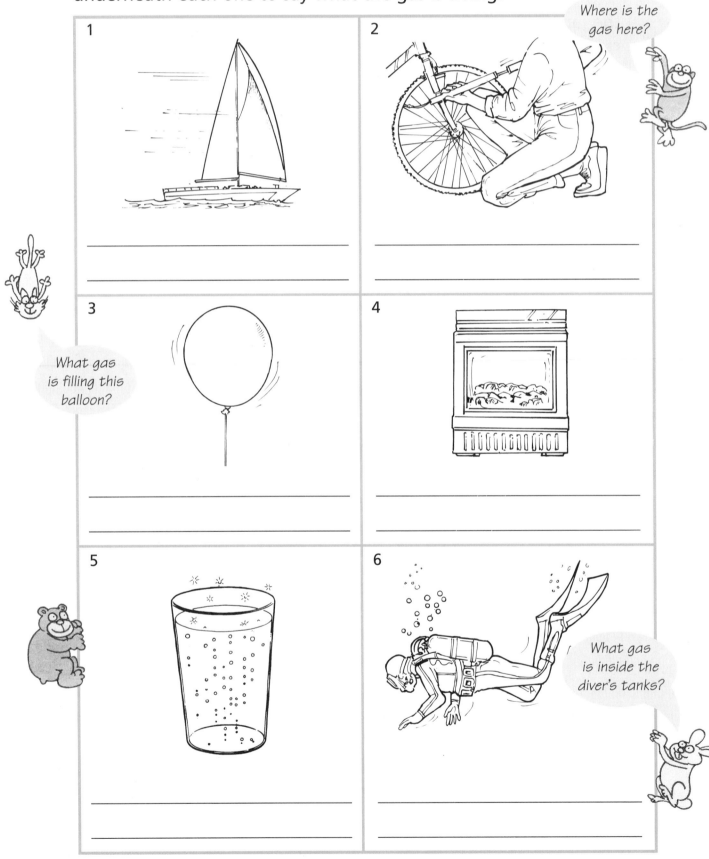

1

2

Where is the gas here?

3

What gas is filling this balloon?

4

5

6

What gas is inside the diver's tanks?

Carnival day

Look at the picture above.

Identify examples of **solids**, **liquids** and **gases** and where they are being used.

Think about this – it's not as easy as it seems!

Solids	Liquids	Gases
	water – for the goldfish	

Fizz, drip, bang

Gases have some **properties** that are different from those of solids and liquids.

Some properties apply to more than one!

1 Complete the table by ticking the properties that apply to solids, liquids and gases.

One has been done for you.

Property	Solid	Liquid	Gas
Has a definite shape.	✔		
Has no definite shape.			
Takes the shape of its container.			
Keeps the same volume.			
Changes its volume.			
Can be poured.			
Has weight.			
Has no weight.			
Flows easily.			
Does not flow easily.			
Some are invisible.			

2 Complete the sentence below by giving all the properties of gases.

A gas has _____

_____

_____

_____

3 Complete these statements to identify the differences between a gas, a solid and a liquid.

(a) These properties make a gas different from a liquid:

_____

_____

_____

(b) These properties make a liquid different from a solid:

_____

_____

_____

4 Now complete this chart, showing how something changes as you heat it up or cool it down.

You'll need to put the words | solid   liquid   gas | in the big boxes.

You'll need to put the words | condenses   melts   evaporates | in the smaller boxes.

Now tick the correct boxes to show whether you need to heat it or cool it.

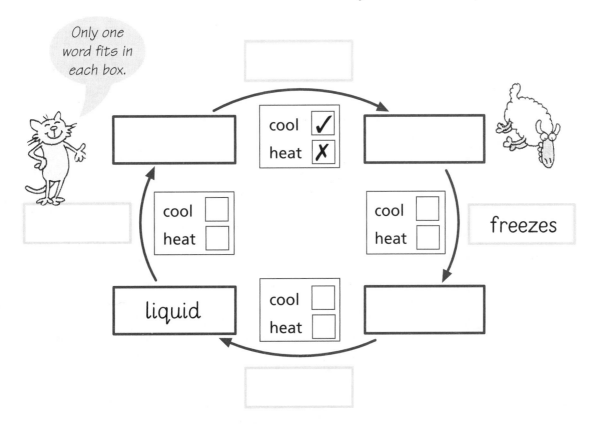

Sounds all around

Study this page for sources of **sounds**.

A

B

C

1 How many sounds do you think that you would be able to hear in each location?

A	B	C

2 Identify the **source** of each of the sounds and make a list of these sources in the table. Describe the sound being produced from each source. Rank the sounds from quietest to loudest.

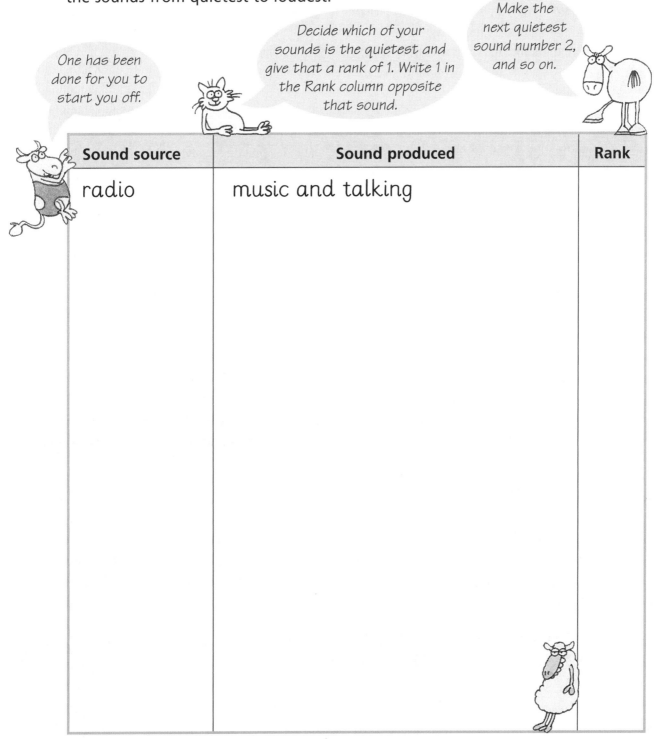

One has been done for you to start you off.

Decide which of your sounds is the quietest and give that a rank of 1. Write 1 in the Rank column opposite that sound.

Make the next quietest sound number 2, and so on.

Sound source	Sound produced	Rank
radio	music and talking	

Loud or quiet?

Sounds can vary in **loudness**. Some sounds are very loud and can be heard from a long way away. Other sounds are very quiet and you can only just hear them. Unpleasant sounds are often called noise.

The level of sound is measured in **decibels**.

We write decibels dB for short.

1 On the decibel scale below decide where the following sounds should go. Draw a picture in the correct box.

heavy traffic	whispering	vacuum cleaner	aircraft engine
children talking	pneumatic drill	rustling leaves	space rocket taking off

Some sounds can be harmful to your hearing. Your hearing is precious so look after it.

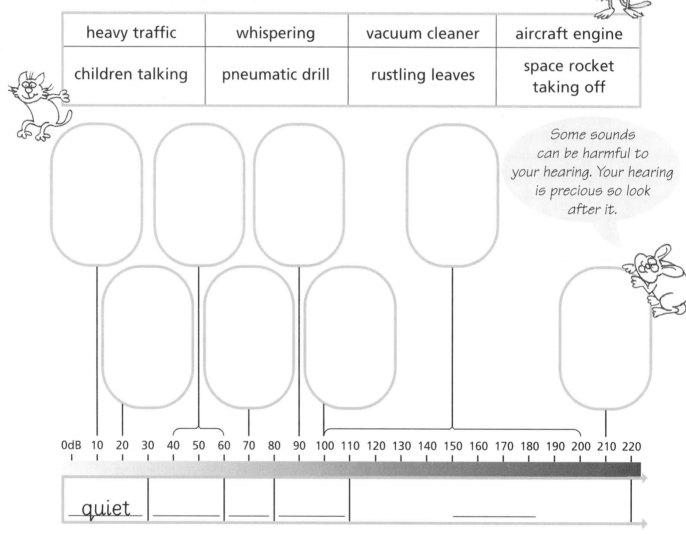

0dB 10 20 30 40 50 60 70 80 90 100 110 120 130 140 150 160 170 180 190 200 210 220

quiet

2 Underneath the scale write these words in the correct order.

danger	quiet	harmful	loud	normal

Were you surprised by any of the measurements?

3 Find other sounds inside and outside the house.
Draw arrows on the scale to show where you think they should go.

54

Good vibrations

A sound is made when something moves backwards and forwards over and over again. We call this **vibrating**.

These vibrations cause the air to move as a **sound wave**. If the sound wave reaches our ear we hear the sound.

Draw a line to join the picture and its explanation.

1 Match the picture to the correct explanation.

| As the tuning fork is put into the glass of water, the water splashes out. This is caused by the vibrations of the tuning fork. | If you put rice on the skin of a drum, the rice jumps up. This is caused by the vibrations of the drum skin. | If you touch your throat when you are talking, you can feel your **vocal cords** vibrating. |

Make your own string telephone.

You will need

- 2 empty plastic cups or yoghurt pots
- 5 m of string

What to do

1 Make a hole in the bottom of each of the pots.
2 Tie a knot in one end of the string and thread the other end through the hole in one of the pots.
3 Thread the string through the other pot and tie a knot in the end of the string.
4 Try your string telephone out with another person.

Ask an adult to help you make the holes. You will probably need to use a sharp point.

Can you make it work around corners?

Can you make a telephone so one person can talk to three others?

Does it work better when the string is tight or slack?

2 Explain how the string telephone works.

_____

_____

_____

Musical instruments

Sound is caused by **vibrating** objects.

Write the answer in the space below the picture.

What is the main thing vibrating in each of the objects below?

Is it
- a column of air?
- skin?
- a string?
- a piece of metal or wood?

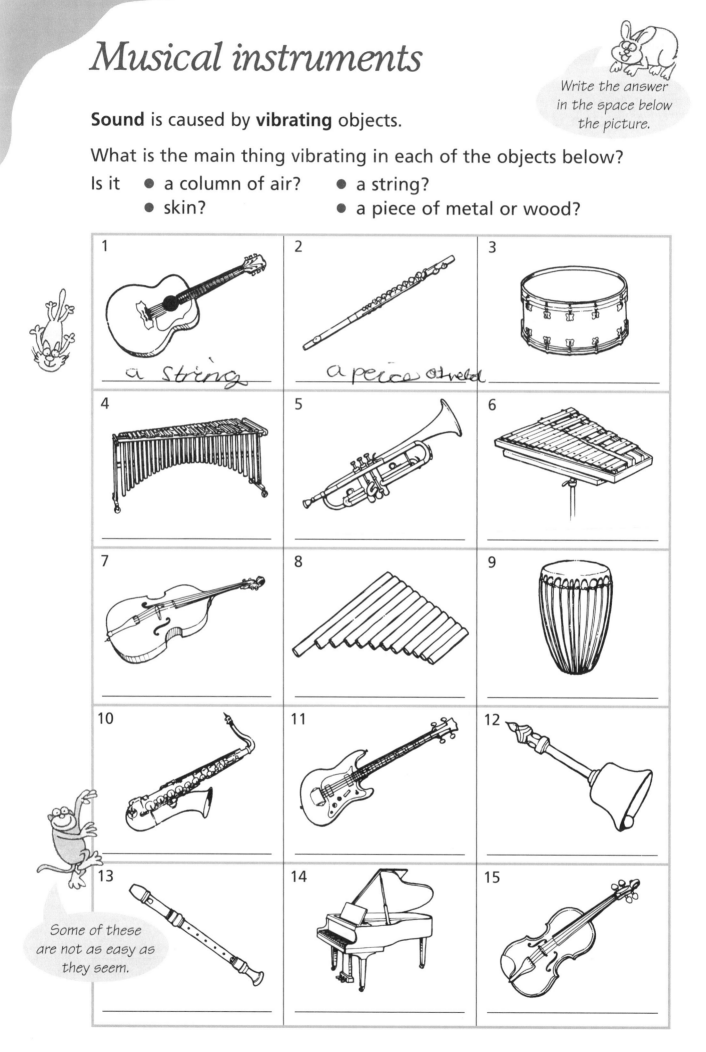

1. a string

2. a peice of wood

3.

4.

5.

6.

7.

8.

9.

10.

11.

12.

13.

14.

15.

Some of these are not as easy as they seem.

56

Pitch

You can change the note by changing the length of the string or column of air.

The shorter the string, the higher the note, and the higher the **pitch**.

1 Look at these pictures. Each one shows a high note or a low note being played. Decide which is which and write 'high' or 'low' under the picture.

 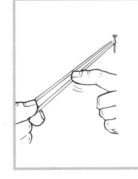 

(a) _____ (b) _____ (c) _____ (d) _____

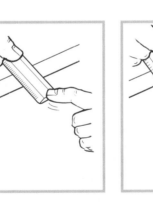 

(e) _____ (f) _____

2 Try tapping the side of a glass bottle partly filled with water. Now change the amount of water in the bottle and tap it again.

What do you notice? _____

_____

_____

3 Why do you think this happens? _____

_____

_____

Pitch change

You can change the **pitch** of sound made by pipes by changing the length of the tube. Yasmin is using a special pipe to see how this works.

This is what her pipe would look like if you cut it in half:

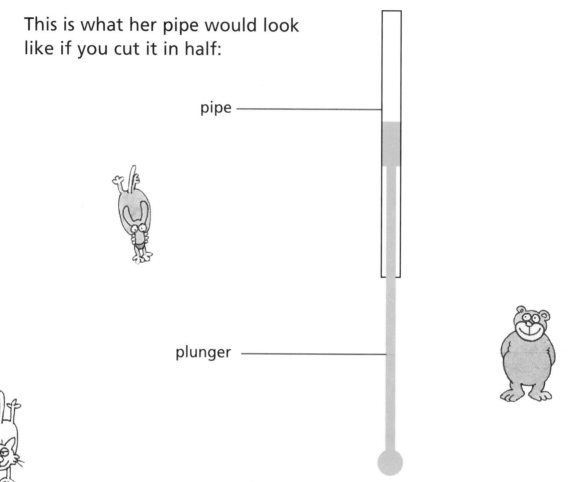

pipe

plunger

1   What happens when Yasmin blows across the top of the pipe? (It's just like blowing across the top of a bottle.)

_____

2   While Yasmin is blowing she pushes the plunger up the tube. What happens to the pitch?

_____

3   She then pulls the plunger down the tube. Now what happens to the pitch?

_____

4   Why does this happen?

_____

_____

Hit it

Percussion instruments have to be **hit** in order to make a sound.

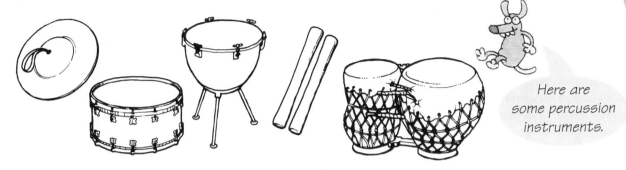

Here are some percussion instruments.

Rita and Ben collected three objects that are hollow and three objects that are solid.

1 Which of the two groups do you think will make better sounds? Why?

_____

_____

_____

_____

Make your own drum kit. Try using saucepans, boxes, tins and other sorts of containers.

2 What could you use for a cymbal? _____

3 Draw a picture of your drum kit in the space below.

Accompany a piece of music using your drum kit.

Travelling sounds

We know **sound travels through air** but does it travel through solids and liquids?

Try these activities to see.

1 Tie some spoons in the middle of a piece of string and jingle them together. Find the ends of the string and press them hard against your ears. Describe the sound you hear.

_____

_____

_____

2 Tap a table and listen to the sound it makes. Lean your head against the table so that your ear is touching the surface. Tap the table underneath and listen to the sound again. What do you notice?

_____

_____

_____

3 Next time you go swimming try this out. Lean your head back so that your ears are under the water. Can you hear any sounds?

_____

_____

4 Does sound travel through water? _____

5 Does sound travel through solids? _____

Did you know there is no sound at all on the Moon? Why do you think this is?

Did you know whales and dolphins can communicate by sound? Why do you think this is?

Sound proofing

Sound travels through some materials better than others. Sometimes we want to block out the sound so we use materials which are good at this. This is called **sound proofing**.

1 Carry out this activity to see which materials are good at sound proofing.

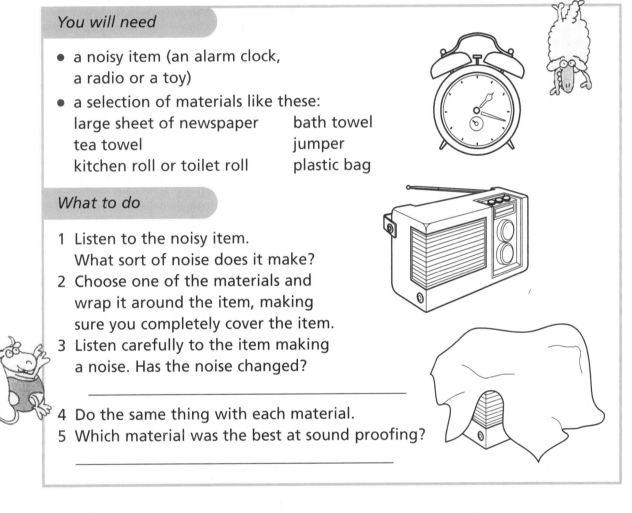

You will need

- a noisy item (an alarm clock, a radio or a toy)
- a selection of materials like these:
  large sheet of newspaper   bath towel
  tea towel   jumper
  kitchen roll or toilet roll   plastic bag

What to do

1 Listen to the noisy item.
  What sort of noise does it make?
2 Choose one of the materials and wrap it around the item, making sure you completely cover the item.
3 Listen carefully to the item making a noise. Has the noise changed?

  _____

4 Do the same thing with each material.
5 Which material was the best at sound proofing?

  _____

2 This test was **unfair**. Make a list of reasons why it is not a fair test.

_____   _____

_____   _____

3 Devise your own test, making sure it is fair. Think about how you would measure the level of sound. Write down your ideas.

_____

_____

_____

_____

Puzzler

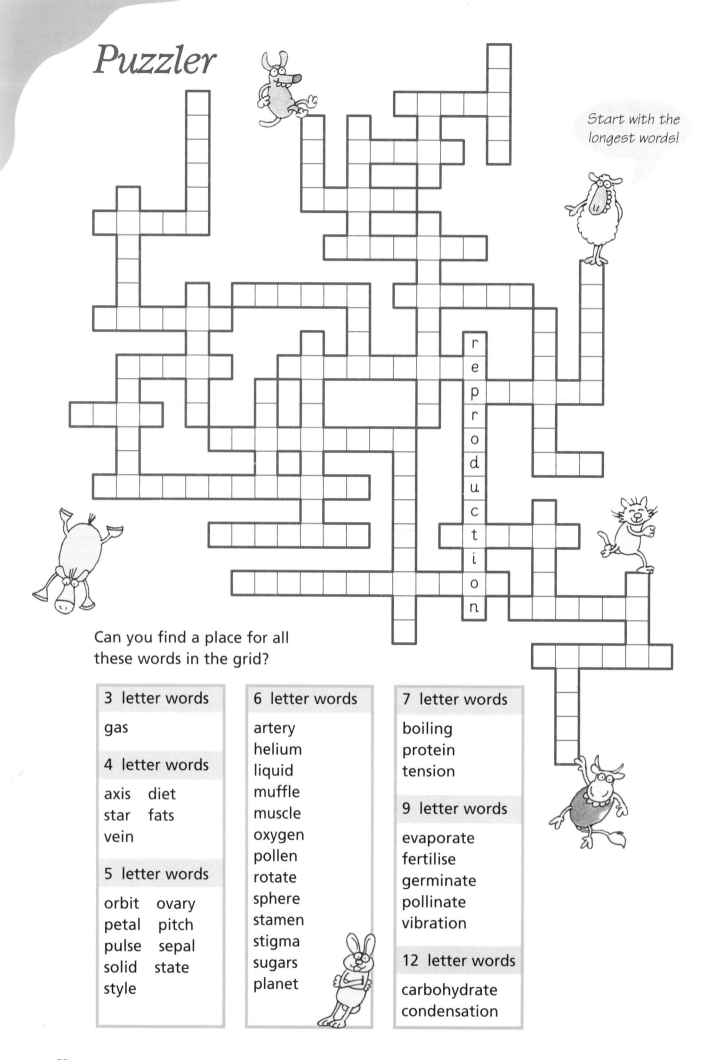

Start with the longest words!

Can you find a place for all these words in the grid?

3 letter words
gas

4 letter words	
axis	diet
star	fats
vein	

5 letter words	
orbit	ovary
petal	pitch
pulse	sepal
solid	state
style	

6 letter words
artery
helium
liquid
muffle
muscle
oxygen
pollen
rotate
sphere
stamen
stigma
sugars
planet

7 letter words
boiling
protein
tension

9 letter words
evaporate
fertilise
germinate
pollinate
vibration

12 letter words
carbohydrate
condensation

Answers and Hints

In some instances there may be more than one possible answer so you may need to check that the answer your child has given is reasonable. As long as your child's answer makes sense and has shown they understand the question, you should mark it right. Sometimes the question will ask them to express an opinion, to make a prediction or to create their own piece of work. When marking your child's efforts please remember that encouragement is always more helpful than criticism.

PAGE 5
1 (ticked fruit) tomato, apple, cucumber, acorn, walnut, peach, raspberry, date, mango, watermelon, runner beans, orange, grape   2 (eat seeds) tomato, cucumber, walnut, runner beans, raspberry; (don't eat seeds) apple, acorn, orange, peach, grape, date, mango, watermelon

PAGE 6
1 Check that your child has labelled the skin, flesh or pulp, and seeds correctly.   2 they contain the seeds that develop into new plants   3 to protect the seed (some also provide food for the new plant)

PAGE 7
1 (A) horse chestnut, acorn, almond; (B) peach, mango, nectarine, avocado; (C) tomato, pepper, cucumber; (D) blackberry, raspberry; (E) strawberry
2 Check that your child has thought up sensible sorting questions, and that any fruit they have sorted have been placed in the correct box according to these questions.

PAGES 8 & 9
1 (connected seeds and descriptions) wind – the seed is blown away..., animal – the seeds stick to the animal's fur..., explosion – the seed pod splits..., water – the seeds floats away   2 (dandelion) wind dispersal, 'wings' help it float on the wind; (burdock) animal dispersal, hooks on the pod attach to animal fur; (lupin) explosion dispersal, seed pod splits open; (coconut) water dispersal, fruit floats in water   3 (a) wind, (b) water, (c) animal, (d) explosion, (e) wind, (f) animal   4 seeds needs space to grow (away from the original plant), plants need enough sunlight and water

PAGE 10
Check that your child followed the instructions correctly and that their drawing is clear and accurate.

PAGE 11
Check that your child has followed the instructions and labelled the flower parts correctly.

PAGES 12 & 13
1 Check that your child has drawn extra stamens and the seeds on their flower. (Check that your child understands that an anther and a filament together are called the stamen, and that the stigma, style and ovule together are called the carpel.)   2 Check that your child has drawn an appropriate insect (e.g. bee, butterfly).

PAGE 14
across: (2) pollen, (4) anther, (6) stamen, (8) petal, (9) ovary
down: (1) filament, (3) carpel, (5) stigma, (7) sepal

PAGE 15
1 (correct order) 1 – The stamen of another flower produces pollen, 2 – Pollen is transferred to the stigma..., 3 – Pollen grains stick to the stigma; 4 – The pollen grain grows a tube..., 5 – The fruit, carrying the new seeds develops   2 by insects or by the wind

PAGE 16
1 & 2 Check that your child has numbered the pictures in the correct order and connected each sentence to the correct picture (2 – The flowers die..., 3 – The seed head is formed, 4 – The seeds are blown away..., 5 – The seed drops onto the soil, 6 – The seed germinates, 7 – The plant begins to grow, 8 – The flowers form).

PAGE 17

i	l	k	j	g	e	r	m	i	n	a	t	i	o	n
s	e	e	d	p	r	o	d	u	c	t	i	o	n	o
u	x	v	f	o	s	t	y	s	l	l	o	h	o	s
i	t	q	e	h	w	s	t	e	p	h	x	b	b	g
l	t	k	r	w	t	z	b	e	y	e	d	g	b	v
t	s	m	t	g	c	p	k	d	c	e	f	z	w	g
x	m	o	i	b	a	e	d	d	q	e	v	y	i	q
u	b	m	l	e	q	w	p	i	g	s	f	u	q	w
i	b	u	i	g	e	k	u	s	g	a	d	u	a	h
k	c	d	s	n	n	r	g	p	t	r	w	j	h	n
o	r	s	a	n	w	c	p	e	m	z	q	f	x	a
i	f	d	t	e	m	z	e	r	p	z	k	a	h	u
n	g	j	i	l	i	v	l	s	j	q	b	h	w	l
q	o	p	o	l	l	i	n	a	t	i	o	n	y	v
u	z	u	n	e	y	p	r	u	t	o	y	j	k	b

2 (life cycle stages, top to bottom) germination, pollination, fertilisation, seed production, dispersal

PAGES 18 & 19
1 Check your child has drawn the pictures for the fly (clockwise from eggs – maggot, pupa, adult fly) and the frog (clockwise from spawn – tadpole, froglet, adult frog) in the correct boxes on page 19.   2 Check sentences are in the correct place for the fly (clockwise from 'egg hatches into a larva (maggot)' – larva changes into a pupa, pupa changes into adult, female adult mates and lays eggs) and the frog (clockwise from after the spawn – egg (spawn) hatches into tadpole, tadpole change into froglet, froglet changes into adult, female adult mates and lays eggs)

PAGES 20 & 21
1 & 2 (number and description, top row) 3 – toddler, 2 – baby, 6 – adult; (bottom row) 1 – embryo, 4 – child, 5 – adolescent   3 child   4 (possible answers) taller, more hair, teeth   5 (possible answers) talk, read, skip   6 (possible similarities) human form develops steadily (no larval phase like a fly), humans mate to produce young   7 (possible differences) humans do not change form during their life cycle, humans do not lay eggs, young humans are dependent upon their parents for a long time   8 Check that your child has researched a life cycle correctly and completed the cycle chart with drawings and descriptions.

PAGES 22 & 23
1 (possible foods, protein) milk, dried beans, cereal, nuts; (carbohydrates) potatoes, baked beans; (fat) butter, cheese, egg yolks, oils, cream, chocolate, cakes; (vitamins and minerals) spinach, tomatoes, milk, lemons, carrots, wheat, cereals, fresh green vegetables   2 Check that your child has kept their record accurately and that they have written the foods in correct boxes.   3 & 4 Check your child's answers – have they given a good reason for their answer?   5 Your child's suggested menu should include a balanced selection of food from the main food groups. (For a vegetarian, the menu won't include meat but should include other protein-rich foods instead.)

PAGES 24 & 25
1 1560 kJ (367 kcal)   2 Check that your child has recorded energy values from several foods correctly (they should include the correct units: either kJ or kcal).   3 & 4 Correct answers will depend on the foods in the chart.   5 (missing value and a possible food combination) dance – 100 kcal, 1 small carton of orange juice + 1 plain biscuit; football – 16 mins, 2 slices of bread; cycle – 40 mins, 3 slices of bread + 2 plain biscuits + 1 apple; sleep – 160 kcal, 1 packet of crisps + 1 plain biscuit; swim – 150 kcal, 3 apples

PAGE 26
1 A typical resting pulse rate is 80–90 beats per minute.   2 Your child should have explained that they would use the middle reading or the average reading.

PAGE 27
1 (highest pulse rate) skipping; (why?) fast exercise using all parts of the body   2 Check your child has correctly calculated this amount from their measurements.   3 (ticked statements) get hotter, feel hot, heart beats faster, feel sweaty, feel tired, breathing speeds up, blood is pumped quicker, muscles work harder

PAGE 28
1 (connected activities and heart rates) playing football – 126 beats per minute, walking – 108, sleeping – 79, sitting writing – 89   2 exercise for same amount of time, start with same pulse rate, use same children each time, measure pulse rate immediately after exercise   3 running   4 pulse rate increases significantly   5 125 beats per minute   6 normal, resting pulse rate

PAGE 29
1 Your child should have coloured red the right half of the heart, plus the vein going into it (on the right) and the artery coming out (top right)   2 Your child should have coloured blue the left half of the heart, plus the vein going into it (top left) and the artery coming out (marked 'to the lungs')   3 (missing numbers, top to bottom) 5, 1, 3, 7, 6, 8, 4, 2

PAGE 30
1 A – jaw, C – elbow, G – knee, D – wrist, H – ankle, E – knuckles, B – shoulder, F – hip   2 The contracted muscles (drawn shortened and fatter) should be coloured red; relaxed muscles (drawn longer and thin) should be blue.

PAGE 31
1 Check that you child has identified only unhealthy things in the picture (some examples: dirty washing up, flies flying around kitchen, adults smoking, girl coughing without covering her mouth, cat and dog eating from the table, children eating fatty and sugary food – chips, burgers, crisps, sweets)   2 Check that your child understands what things are unhealthy, and can explain why the four things they chose are unhealthy.

PAGE 32
Check that your child has depicted their chosen topic well, and that he or she understands the reason why the topic is important.

PAGE 33
1 Check that your child has coloured yellow the side of the Earth facing the Sun, and has coloured the other side grey (in both pictures).   2 B (night in British Isles), A (day in British Isles)   3 Check that your child understands and has explained their reasoning (example: The Earth rotates once on its axis every 24 hours. It is daytime on the part of the Earth that faces the Sun because the light shines on it. It is night-time on the part of the Earth that faces away from the Sun because it is in shadow.).

PAGES 34 & 35
1 (Earth) tennis ball; (Sun) beachball; (Moon) pea   2 Check that your child has written 'sphere' in the chart (under 'Shape') for all three objects (Earth, Sun and Moon).   3 A – Earth, planet, orbits the Sun, made of rock and

metal; B – Moon, satellite, orbits Earth, made of rock and metal; C – Sun, star, a burning ball which gives out light, made of gas   4 'What is it?' and 'What is it made of?' columns in the chart should read (Earth) planet, rock and metal, (Sun) star, gas, (Moon) satellite, rock and metal

PAGE 36
1 Check that your child has labelled the Sun, Earth and Moon correctly.
2 Check that the two orbits are coloured red (Earth round Sun) and blue (Moon round Earth), and that your child has coloured the small key as well.
3 365 (the orbit is actually a little longer and is not an exact number of days; we use leap years to make up for this)   4 months

PAGE 37
1 full   2 sun   3 Moon   4 phases   5 crescent   6 man   7 shadow   8 new
9 orbit   10 cheese   The shaded letters read 'lunar month' (a lunar month is 28 days long)

PAGES 38 & 39
1 (length of days in hours, left to right) 15, $13\frac{1}{2}$, 12, $10\frac{1}{2}$, 9, $7\frac{1}{2}$ 2 (a) 08:30, (b) 21:15   3 (a) 16:45, (b) 20:30   4 Check that you child has completed the bar chart correctly (at heights corresponding to (June to Dec) $16\frac{1}{2}$ hours, 15 hours, $13\frac{1}{2}$ hours, 12 hours, $10\frac{1}{2}$ hours, 9 hours and $7\frac{1}{2}$ hours).   5 (a) June, (b) $16\frac{1}{2}$ 6 (a) December, (b) $7\frac{1}{2}$ 7 9   8 Check that your child understands the pattern in the bar chart (days are short in winter and longer in summer, and there is approximately $1\frac{1}{2}$ hours more or less daylight each month).

PAGE 40
Check your child's drawing and the facts they have used in their writing are correct.

PAGE 41
1 the water disappeared/dried up   2 salt crystals   3 evaporation

PAGE 42
1 (a) some of the water in the puddle has evaporated, (b) wind and sunlight have dried out the clothes (all the water has evaporated)   2 Check your child understands what happens to water when it evaporates. The drawings should show 'before and after' drawings of a sensible situation where water has evaporated.

PAGE 43
1 A possible example experiment is to use two saucers containing water. One could be left in a warm place (on a window sill in the sun, near the radiator) and the other in a cool place (in a cool cupboard, in the fridge). The amounts of water left in each saucer after a set time (say a days or several hours) can then be compared. To make the test fair, your child would need to use the same amount of water (and the same shaped saucer) in each case.   2 Your child should be able to predict that the water will evaporate quicker in a warm place.

PAGE 44
1 water   2 from the water vapour in the air   3 the cold surfaces cooled the gas (water vapour) and water droplets formed (turned from a gas to a liquid)   4 condensation   5 Check that your child has thought up two other examples of condensation (possible answers: condensation on tiles in the kitchen while cooking, cloud formation is a condensation process)

PAGE 45
1 (picture labels, left to right) solid, liquid, gas   2 (graph labels, left to right) solid, liquid, gas   3 0˚C   4 100˚C   5 100˚C   6 0˚C

PAGE 46
1 A – clouds form…, B – the cloud cools…, C – water vapour rises from the sea, D – water vapour rises from the rivers and lakes, E – water flows back into the sea   2 in the sea, rivers and lakes, and from the land   3 in the sky to make clouds

PAGE 47
1 (clockwise from top right) ice, condensation, water, drips   2 Your child's explanations should show that they understand the processes in this experiment (the hot water evaporates and rises, and when it comes into contact with a cold surface, the water in the air condenses and drips as water back down into the water).

PAGE 48
1 The moving air is being caught by the sails and is pushing the boat along.
2 The pump is compressing the air and forcing it into the tyre to inflate it.
3 The gas in the balloon is lighter than air so the balloon rises (the gas is probably helium).   4 The gas is burning and giving off heat.   5 Gas bubbles in the lemonade make the drink fizzy.   6 The diver fills his tanks with air so that he can breathe under water.

PAGE 49
There are lots of possible answers – whatever your child has written, check that they understand where the solid, liquid or gas is and what it's doing.

PAGES 50 & 51
1 (ticked properties, solid) has a definite shape, keeps the same volume, has weight, does not flow easily; (liquid) has no definite shape, takes the shape of its container, keeps the same volume, can be poured, has weight, flows easily; (gas) has no definite shape, takes the shape of its container, changes its volume, has weight, flows easily, some are invisible   2 (possible sentence) A gas has no definite shape, takes the shape of its container, changes its volume, has weight, flows easily and some are invisible.   3 (a) it changes its volume and some are invisible; (b) it has no definite shape, takes the shape of its container, can be poured and flows easily   4 (big boxes, clockwise from top left) gas, liquid, solid, liquid; (small boxes, clockwise from top) condenses, freezes, melts, evaporates; (ticked boxes, clockwise from top) cool, cool, heat, heat

PAGES 52 & 53
1 (A) at least 8 sounds – washing machine, running taps, handling crockery, stirring teapot, chopping, radio, television, boiling kettle; (B) at least 6 sounds – bird singing, plane flying over, tractor, chainsaw, sheep, river running; (C) at least 6 sounds – dog barking, newspaper man shouting, people talking, cars and trucks driving, firetruck sirens, person rollerblading
2 Check your child has filled in the chart sensibly – if you think that their ranking (from loud to noisy) is wrong talk to them about the different types of sound and how noisy the different things are likely to be.

PAGE 54
1 (filled in boxes, top row, left to right) whispering, children talking, heavy traffic, aircraft engine; (bottom row) rustling leaves, vacuum cleaner, pneumatic drill, space rocket taking off   2 (missing words, left to right) normal, loud, harmful, danger   3 Check where your child has written their own sounds – have they placed them sensibly on the chart?

PAGE 55
1 (connected pictures and descriptions) drum – If you put rice…, talking person – If you touch your throat…, glass of water – As the tuning fork…
2 Your child's answer should show that they understand that the sound of the speaker's voice makes the string vibrate and the sound travels along the string to the listener's ear.

PAGE 56
1 string   2 column of air   3 skin   4 piece of metal or wood   5 column of air   6 piece of metal or wood   7 string   8 column of air   9 skin
10 column of air   11 string   12 piece of metal   13 column of air   14 string
15 string

PAGE 57
1 (a) low, (b) high, (c) low, (d) high, (e) high, (f) low   2 the pitch of the sound becomes lower when there is more water is in the bottle   3 Your child should understand that the glass can vibrate more easily (and therefore more quickly to make a higher pitched sound) when the bottle is empty (the water in the bottle slows down the vibration and makes a lower pitched sound).

PAGE 58
1 the pipe makes a sound   2 the pitch gets higher   3 the pitch gets lower
4 vibrations are produced in the column of air in the pipe; the pitch gets higher when the column of air is shorter

PAGE 59
1 the hollow objects will make better sounds; hollow objects can vibrate more freely and make bigger sound waves   2 Your child could use saucepan lids to make cymbals.   3 Check your child's drawing – how much noise did their drum kit make!?

PAGE 60
1 the sound is louder and deeper   2 the sound is louder and deeper   3 the sound is muffled but can still be heard   4 & 5 Your child should understand that sound can travel through liquids and solids but it changes (it sounds different).   There is no sound on the Moon because there is no atmosphere to carry the sound waves. Whales and dolphins communicate by sending out sound waves that travel through water.

PAGE 61
1 Check that your child carried out the activity as described and has kept a note of the results. Encourage your child to draw conclusions based on their results.   2 the thickness of the materials (and their size) are different, the sounds all have different volumes, judging changes in sound is difficult (it isn't measured precisely in this experiment)   3 Check that your child's test is practical and fair (in a fair test only one thing is changed each time, keeping everything else in the experiment the same). This is a difficult experiment to do, because your child needs to be able to compare sound levels. One way would be to use a tape recorder to record what the noisy item sounds like each time (an alarm clock would reliably produce the same amount of noise every time). Your child could then play back all the recordings one after another and would then be able to judge the ranking, from loudest to quietest.

PAGE 62